To Milt
To me, one of the
"giants" and
a major influence
always
Gratefully
Bob

Staring Night:
Queen Victoria's Late-Life Depression

Staring Night:
Queen Victoria's
Late-Life Depression

Robert C. Abrams

International Psychoanalytic Books (IPBooks)

New York • http://www.IPBooks.net

Staring Night: Queen Victoria's Late-Life Depression

Published by IPBooks, Queens, NY
Online at: www.IPBooks.net

ISBN: 978-1-949093-55-1

Let me imagine that we will come
        again
when we want to and it will be spring
we will be no older than we ever were
the worn griefs will have eased like
        the early cloud
through which the morning slowly
        comes to itself
and the ancient defenses against the
        dead
will be done with and left to the dead
        at last
the light will be as it is now in the
        garden
that we have made here these years
        together
of our long evenings and
        astonishment

From "To Paula in the Late Spring," in *The Shadow of Sirius* by W.S. Merwin. Bloodaxe Books, Eastburn, UK, 2009.

"I don't want to live to be very old; the penalties are too great."

The Hon. Marie Adeane Mallet, Lady in Waiting to Queen Victoria, 1900

Contents

1.   Introduction: Queen Victoria's Last Months and the Final Volume of Her Personal Journal

There were princesses standing up in their carriages, and black men from the Gold Coast, Maharajahs from India, and red-coated Tommys, and young men who will inherit kingdoms and empires.... There was probably never before such a moment, in which so many races of people, of so many castes, and of such different values to this world, sang praises to God at one time, and in one place and with one heart. And when it was all over, and the cannon at the Tower were booming across the water-front, the Archbishop of Canterbury, of all the people in the world, waved his arm and shouted 'Three cheers for the Queen!' and the soldiers stuck their bear-skins on their bayonets and swung them above their heads and cheered, and the women on the housetops and balconies waved their handkerchiefs and cheered, and the Lady in the Black Dress nodded and bowed her head at them, and winked away the tears in her eyes.

From *A Year From A Reporter's Notebook* by Richard Harding Davis. Harper & Brothers, New York and London, 1903. This excerpt describes Queen Victoria's Diamond Jubilee marking the 60th year of her reign (1837–1897).

"From my heart I thank my beloved people. May God bless them! Victoria RI" (telegraphic message from the Queen to the people of Britain and the Empire following the Jubilee, 1897).

So concluded the apex of Queen Victoria's life. In two brief but emotion-filled sentences—gracious, sincere and even rather intimate—Queen Victoria thanked the British people for all that they had accomplished in her name through the crowded but superbly successful decades following her coronation in 1837. But from this point forward, and especially during the last five months of her life, Queen Victoria herself declined steadily in health and spirit.

The Queen's failing health was at least indirectly the consequence of her grief over a deluge of losses: Three of her nine children had died, with a fourth actively dying, and she had also seen the deaths of a score or more of her closest friends and intimates. Her ability to function had ebbed steadily, culminating in the loss of eyesight, ambulation, strength and memory, but most cruelly in a state of depression that deprived her of vitality, sleep and appetite. It was fortunate for Queen Victoria that in the final years of the 19th century, her public, political and ceremonial roles had all culminated in spectacular successes, because the personal suffering she endured during her last year of life, particularly in the closing months of 1900, was truly terrible.

In this book, the illness and death of Queen Victoria will be portrayed as exemplars of the devastating effects of depression in old age. From an old-age physician's perspective, the final volume of Queen Victoria's personal Journal reveals that during the last five months of her life, the Queen suffered from late-life depression, a specific age-related mood disorder.

Brought on by a complex interaction among different factors, including cerebrovascular disease, functional disabilities, and the number and weight of her losses, the melancholia experienced by the Queen at the end of her life differed in many ways from her prolonged mourning after the death of her husband Prince Albert in 1861. Yet it has been the more colorful and melodramatic earlier depression, not the later one, that has lived on in the popular imagination. Still, the depression experienced by the aged Queen Victoria had great, if underappreciated, importance. Distinct from her histrionic grieving for Albert, the Queen's depression in old age contributed crucially to her demise. This is not only the central thesis of the present book but also the rationale for a fresh perspective on one of Britain's most extensively documented monarchs.

It can be said that Queen Victoria's late-life depression was partially caused by, and also confounded, a spiraling descent into physical disability. Weight loss and muscular atrophy in turn contributed to progressively worsening weakness. Then, while there is no direct evidence for significant memory loss anywhere in the final volume of the Journal, it almost certainly occurred, gossiped about among courtiers more than it was ever documented. The Queen had in fact been acquiring cerebrovascular changes over a period of years—an accumulation of small lesions that eventually became decisive in their totality.

These cerebrovascular events could themselves be viewed as either cause or effect: Vascular changes, now considered to be mediated by inflammatory processes (Alexopoulos & Morimoto, 2011), are known to produce a vulnerability to depression in older people; and the weakening effects of depression can contribute a vulnerability to vascular events. For Queen Victoria, personal losses and physical disabilities also influenced each other reciprocally, resulting in a sharply downward trend during the last year of the Queen's life.

In *Staring Night* Queen Victoria's final five months of life will be examined using an analysis of entries from the concluding volume of the Journal she had kept since the age of 14. The last volume of the Queen's Journal chronicles the events and the illness that culminated in her death; and this record will be used as a primary source to enlarge a late-life portrait of the Queen (Chapters 2–5).* Later chapters describe in detail the death of the Queen (Chapter 6) and survey the clinical science of late-life depression as it might have applied to Queen Victoria (Chapters 7–10).

---

* **Author's note:** Chapters 2 through 5 cover the events and background of Queen Victoria's Journal entries as she moves from Osborne House on the Isle of Wight, where she has spent most of the summer of 1900 (Chapter 2), to Balmoral Castle in Scotland for the fall (Chapter 3), to Windsor Castle for the late fall (Chapter 4), and then back to Osborne for Christmas (Chapter 5). The entire Journal has been in the public domain since 2012, and selected entries from the last volume are excerpted in these chapters.

For Chapters 2 through 5, a discussion precedes each related Journal entry or group of entries. Footnotes are used to identify key individuals.

The Journal entries are presented in italics. Non-italic font has been used in brackets for editorial comments or explanations placed within the italicized Journal entries.

In reproducing the selected Journal entries, Queen Victoria's own punctuation marks have been copied as closely as possible, for example, her intermittent use of periods followed by long dashes for the end of complete sentences within the text, usually before a change of topic (.—), and shorter dashes following periods in cases where the day's Journal entry has been concluded at that point (.–). Queen Victoria and her posthumous Journal editor Princess Beatrice followed these general rules, but not always consistently.

Parts of the Journal entries have been omitted because of redundancy or lack of direct relevance. For this purpose, ellipses (…) indicate that the words or phrases removed had been within a single sentence. The designation (….) is used to show that the omitted words or phrases had completed a sentence in the original entry. A short dash followed by an ellipsis (– …) signals that one or more whole sentences have been deleted.

An area in which the logic of rules can be particularly difficult to discern is the abbreviation of social, professional and military titles in the Queen's Journal entries. Here the conventions for superscripting, underlining, or placing periods and colons, vary widely, depending on the title, as for M^r., D^r, L^d, P^{ss}, Capt:, Col:, etc.

Letters by Queen Victoria, family members, Governmental officials or courtiers, and contributions from other contemporaneous sources are also excerpted but placed within the general text and not italicized. However, longer or more important excerpts from these sources are indented from the surrounding text and the quotation marks removed, except for single quotation marks where the letter-writer is making a verbatim citation. Ellipses to indicate removed words, phrases or sentences have been used in the letter excerpts, but largely without Queen Victoria's idiosyncratic style of short and long dashes.

Dates are noted as, for example, 1 January 1901, to be consistent with the Queen's practice in her Journal.

In all other areas standard American spelling, punctuation, and style have been used.

Writing about Queen Victoria

One of the greatest difficulties in writing about Queen Victoria—a challenge faced by the many who attempt to do so—is how to reconcile the disparate aspects of her inconsistent and often contradictory personality. These contradictions tended to become more and more pronounced during the Queen's long widowhood. The fact that in Prince Albert's absence no one in her immediate family, least of all her children, dared to question the Sovereign on personal matters may have allowed her eccentricities to harden into permanence. In a famous summation, Elizabeth, Lady Longford, used a string of paired opposites to capture the Queen's personality as a whole (St. John Parker, 2007, p. 20): "Unselfish and inconsiderate, tactful and blunt, sympathetic and hard, patient and fidgety, direct and devious, irresistibly charming and bristling with repellent power."

Accordingly, biographical accounts have mirrored these differences, ranging in tone from hagiographic (Strachey, 1921) to more realistic (Arnstein, 2003; Hibbert, 2000; Weintraub, 1988). Lytton Strachey's *Queen Victoria*, a prime example of the former, is blatantly adulatory—so much so that King George V was said to have been angered by it, interpreting the work as an insulting caricature of his revered grandmother (Rose, 1984). As a further example of his excess, Strachey, when describing the change in the public's attitude toward the Queen as the end of her reign approached, wrote (Strachey, 1921, p. 406): "In the dazzled imagination of her subjects Victoria soared aloft towards the regions of divinity through a nimbus of purest glory." A similar divide can be observed in more recent accounts, where one can find both fawning and critical portrayals. While mostly in the former camp, the published memoirs and letters of several of the Queen's most devoted ladies, the Hon. Marie Mallet*† (Mallet, 1968) and Edith, Lady Lytton,‡ (Lutyens, 1962) still manage to be fair and thoughtful at critical junctures.

Biographers' admiration for the subjects whose portraits they create is probably at least as harmful to balance as open contempt or rejection, if not more so. Ernest Jones (1953), in a preface to the seminal, three-volume biography of his beloved mentor, Sigmund Freud, boasts that he had recognized and "worked through" his "hero-worshipping propensities" before ever encountering Freud personally. However, from the very first pages immediately following the preface, Jones' readers are given good reason to question the thoroughness of his self-analysis in this area. The book itself is dedicated by Jones to Anna Freud, "true daughter of an immortal sire."

Queen Victoria's Journal

The Queen's accounts of her last five months of life present an often-moving "Book of Pain," in which her physical decline and personal losses are described, elaborated, and lamented. By the summer of 1900 the Queen could no longer see well enough to pen Journal entries herself, nor, toward

---

* The Hon. Mrs. Bernard Mallet, née Marie Adeane, who came from a family with close connections to the Royal house extending over several generations, had first been appointed Maid of Honour to Queen Victoria from 1887 to 1891. After her marriage to Bernard Mallet she rejoined the Queen's Household as an Extra Woman of the Bedchamber in 1895, returning to be with her at regular intervals until 19 November 1900. Like all who served Queen Victoria, Mrs. Mallet had pledged not to keep a journal or diary, but she sidestepped this restriction by recording much of what she saw and heard in frequent letters to her family. From these letters, later edited and published by her son, Victor, many of the most interesting and revealing observations of Queen Victoria in her later years are drawn.

† The Queen gave the close female members of her Household who were not peers' daughters the style of "Honourable," with the rank of Barons' daughters.

‡ Edith Bulwer-Lytton, Countess of Lytton, was a Lady of the Bedchamber to Queen Victoria from 1895 to 1901.

the end, did she have the strength to do so. For that reason the entries in the last volume of her Journal, beginning on 17 August, 1900 and ending on 13 January, 1901, nine days before her death on the 22nd, were mostly dictated to whichever daughter or granddaughter happened to be staying with her at the time. However, the majority were inscribed by "Thora," Princess Helena Victoria of Schleswig-Holstein, a devoted, much-loved granddaughter and intimate of the Queen. "Thora" was an unmarried daughter of Princess Christian, the Queen's third daughter, who lived with her family at Cumberland Lodge in Windsor Great Park [see also Appendices and footnotes].

The Journal itself, an engrossing archive relied upon by many historians, has nevertheless been regarded as a compromised primary source. After the Queen's death, her youngest daughter and *de facto* literary executor, Princess Beatrice, heavily edited the document. Over a thirty-year period, the Princess rewrote the entire Journal, volume by volume, first into draft forms, which she then laboriously copied onto permanent blue notebooks, burning both the original and draft volumes as she proceeded. These blue notebooks, all in the Princess' neatly legible hand, are today preserved in the Royal Archives at Windsor Castle. In 2012, in response to increasing public interest and in honor of the Jubilee of Queen Elizabeth II, the complete Journal was scanned and made available on the internet.

Presumably, Princess Beatrice edited in accord with the late Queen's wishes but probably also did so with a view to how she wanted posterity to understand her formidable mother. Still, exactly what the Princess redacted or changed can never be known. Embarrassing or even scandalous passages reflecting Queen Victoria's romantic feelings about her servant John Brown? Excesses of self-pity? Perhaps some early evidence of cognitive impairment that had been withheld from the public? But whatever may have been lost, the overall style and authenticity of the Queen's writing are likely to have been preserved; and her uniquely contradictory voice, sometimes deliberate and wise, at other times impulsive and naïve, appears to have survived the conflagration of the original volumes.

Queen Victoria's Journal is above all personal, even trivial at times, for the most part avoiding or de-emphasizing political events. However, on the rare occasions when matters of State are referenced within the pages of the Journal, the Queen seems to retain an excellent command of detail, even as her health dramatically declines. Her impressive grasp of affairs is on view, for example, in the entries discussing the rotation of ministries in the cabinet of her last Prime Minister, Lord Salisbury. Here she demonstrates the mastery of *realpolitik* she had acquired over a nearly 63-year reign.

The Journal is the most important and complete surviving document that reveals the Queen's own account of events and a reflection of her emotional life. Highlighted within its pages are her day-to-day activities, relationships with family and officials of the Royal Household, details of her deteriorating health, and her views on matters large and small. As a rule, the last volume of the Journal emphasizes the emotional and expressive aspects of Queen Victoria's nature over the shrewd, practical and commonsense qualities she had often displayed throughout her reign. Within the pages of her Journal she felt a freedom to express her genuine self, aside from her position; and in so doing she was able to find an authentic literary voice, showcasing both the hubris and the more appealing aspects of her personality.

Among the features of Queen Victoria's Journal that make it so unique and interesting is the singular style she developed to express her thoughts. She made no attempt to achieve fairness or balance. Instead the reader is impressed by a highly developed and distinctive use of language. Except on those occasions when her physical pain is worse than she wishes to acknowledge, at which times she tends to dissemble gently, Queen Victoria is categorical and definitive in the way she phrases and punctuates. The reader of the final volume of Her Majesty's Journal is thus treated to fresh, exuberant prose despite the bitter onslaught of events. It is difficult to imagine that the Queen did not intend this affecting self-portrait to be read by future generations, to learn what they could of Victoria the person and the adversities of aging that she faced.

Although self-referential in the sense that all personal journals inevitably are, what is missing here is the blatant selfishness that was among the features of the Queen's personality. Also notably absent is her anger. In fact, while the Queen on a few occasions is hyperbolic, in the final volume of her Journal the range of Victoria's expressed emotion mostly narrows, from self-pity when referring to herself, to empathy for others who have suffered similar losses. But Queen Victoria's Journal could never be described as a mirror of insightful introspection; nor is it a confessional, as one might expect from contemporary Journals and memoirs.

Rather, the final volume of the Journal tells the story of an aging woman who, with an artistic sensibility and an unrelenting focus on her own physical and emotional self, experiences depression as a gathering, unstoppable force. In her entries spanning the last five months of her life, Queen Victoria describes how she is shaken by losses and weakened by insomnia and anorexia. The darkening days of the late autumn and early winter of 1900, on which she comments repeatedly, provide a somber backdrop to the rapid unfolding of her decline.

The entries in the final volume of the Journal typically begin with a description of the weather, then move on to what drives she took during the day and with whom (an exclusively female cast of daughters, granddaughters, daughters-in-law, and Ladies of the Royal Household accompanied her on these drives). "Going out," an activity in which she persisted until the last few days of her life, seems to have been a much-needed tonic for the Queen and became something of a ritual. The notes for each date often conclude with a list of names of the family members, courtiers, and guests who "dined" with her on that evening.

Beginning in mid-August, 1900, shortly after the death of her second son[*] from cancer, Journal entries from the again-grieving Queen deal with family matters and events, with an emphasis on recent or anticipated deaths. From the summer of that year into the fall, the entries also return repeatedly to the vexing disruptions of her appetite and patterns of sleep and her declines in energy and spirit.

Ultimately, it is Queen Victoria's Journal, as revised by Princess Beatrice, that presents the gentlest, most sympathetic view of the Monarch and her reign. Regardless of how the document is read, it is the Journal's final volume, more so than the Queen's extensive and unabridged personal letters, that highlights in detail the onset, course, and dénouement of the depressive disorder from which she suffered throughout the last five months of her life. Although it will be presented in this book with a clinical subtext, at its core this is a human story.

The 17 August 1900 start-date of the final volume of Queen Victoria's Journal is entirely arbitrary; the entries simply take up where Princess Beatrice had run out of space in the preceding (in this case the penultimate) blue notebook. But even if guided by neither literary nor historical considerations, the concluding Journal volume, by a chronological coincidence, happens to encompass the entire five-month course of Queen Victoria's last and lethal depression.

---

[*] Prince Alfred, Duke of Edinburgh, was the second son and fourth child of Queen Victoria and Prince Albert. Known in the family as "Affie," he was also Duke of Saxe-Coburg and Gotha (in lieu of Queen Victoria herself, because under Salic law women were not eligible to succeed to the Dukedom in Coburg).

References

Alexopoulos, G.S., & Morimoto, S.S. (2011). The inflammation hypothesis in geriatric depression. *International Journal of Geriatric Psychiatry 26*, 1109–1118.

Arnstein, W.L. (2003). *Queen Victoria.* Palgrave Macmillan: New York, NY.

Hibbert, C. (2000). *Queen Victoria: A personal history.* Da Capo Press: Cambridge, MA, p. 163.

Lutyens, M. (Ed.). (1962). *Lady Lytton's court diary: 1895–1899.* Rupert Hart-Davis: London, UK.

Mallet, V. (Ed.). (1968). *Life with Queen Victoria: Marie Mallet's letters from Court, 1887–1901.* Houghton Mifflin Company: Boston, MA.

Rose, K. (1984). *King George V.* Alfred A. Knopf: New York, NY, p. 315.

St. John Parker, M. (2007). *Queen Victoria: A Pitkin Guide.* Pitkin Publishing Limited: Singapore, p. 20.

Strachey, L. (1921). *Queen Victoria.* Harcourt Brace Jovanovich: New York; [First Harvest/HB edition, New York, NY, 1978], p. 406.

Weintraub, S. (1988). *Victoria: An intimate biography.* Truman Talley Books/ E.P. Dutton: New York, NY.

2.   Osborne House from 17 August to 31 August, 1900: *"This ever dear day."*

The opening entry (17 August) of the final volume of Queen Victoria's Journal leaves the impression that the Queen has been passing a pleasant summer at Osborne, a house she deeply loves, whose design reflected Albert's collaboration with the builder-architect Cubitt. This was in every sense a family home rather than an official residence, the place where her children were raised and the setting in which in later years she felt most comfortable, with the possible exception of Balmoral (which she loved in a somewhat different way, as a place to withdraw even farther from the center of government and rusticate in the bracing Scottish chill). Throughout her long widowhood, she usually came twice each year to Osborne, typically from mid-July until the end of the third week in August, and again for the Christmas holidays, from mid-December until the end of the third week in February (Hibbert, 2000).

The summer weather at Osborne this year has been particularly fine. Even after the death of her son Affie at the end of July, the Queen continues her habit of breakfasting outdoors in her tent, and in what seems to be the beginning of a reversal of her longstanding preference for cold, now relishing, rather than complaining, about the hot temperatures.

On 17 August the news from the South African front is mostly positive, and the Queen is in good spirits. She enjoys the company of her daughter

Princess Christian* and her grandson's wife, May, neither of whom were the liveliest of companions; but Princess May† (at this time the Duchess of York) she especially admires for her qualities of seriousness, industry, and discretion.

The Journal entry of 17 August also contains a reference to the accomplishments of Prince Louis of Battenberg, the husband of Princess Victoria of Hesse. Princess Victoria was a spirited, freethinking young woman and the grandchild with whom Queen Victoria had corresponded most regularly over the years. In this entry the Queen alludes to Prince Louis's growing reputation as an outstanding naval officer, inspirational leader and astute manager of affairs. Queen Victoria had been pleased to see this granddaughter, whom she had recognized from a young age to have

---

* Princess Christian of Schleswig-Holstein was the third daughter and fifth child of Queen Victoria and Prince Albert. Princess Helena by birth and Princess Christian by marriage, she was known in the family by the diminutive "Lenchen."

† Princess Victoria Mary (May) of Teck (1867–1953) was the daughter of eccentric parents, Queen Victoria's first cousin Princess Mary Adelaide of Cambridge and the morganatic German Prince, Francis Duke of Teck. (The house of Teck had for centuries been absorbed into the Württemberg line but was revived as a princely title for Francis, who had been barred from the Württemberg succession because his mother was not a Princess). Princess Mary Adelaide was famously obese and her husband taciturn and touchy about his semi-royal status. However, the couple's daughter May became a protégé of Queen Victoria, who admired her for her values, intelligence and reliable temperament. Rescuing Princess May from her awkward situation as a not-quite-royal princess whose marital prospects were spurned by nearly all of the Continental royal houses, Queen Victoria chose her to be a future Queen Consort, affiancing her first to the ultimate heir to the throne, Prince Albert Victor of Wales and then, on his untimely death, to his brother, the new heir, Prince George of Wales (Duke of York). Princess May thus became, successively, Duchess of York (1893–1901), Duchess of Cornwall and York (1901), Princess of Wales (1901–1910), Queen Consort to her husband King George V (1910–1936), and Queen Mother (1936–1952). In the last year of her life, 1953, when her granddaughter had succeeded as Elizabeth II and her daughter-in-law Elizabeth became Queen Mother, May was known simply as Queen Mary.

There is ample evidence that Queen Victoria was satisfied with her choice of Princess May. On 9 October 1897, four years after the wedding of Princess May and Prince George, the Queen wrote to her granddaughter-in-law, using her characteristic excess of ampersands: "Each time I see you I love & respect you more & am so truly thankful that Georgie has such a partner—to help & encourage him in his difficult position" (Victoria, R.I., 1897).

been gifted with an intelligent and original outlook, marry another person of exceptional talent. Unlike nearly everyone around her, the Queen cared little about the purity of Royal descent, and, to her, it made scant difference that Louis Battenberg, because of a non-royal mother, was of relatively low rank in the *Almanach de Gotha*, no more so than had the paternal morganatic lineage of Princess May.

For Queen Victoria, the first half of the year 1900 had seen important and gratifying events. The war in South Africa, pitting the world's most powerful empire against a motley group of Afrikaner farmers, had proved more difficult and had lasted longer than anyone expected; but at last, by the spring of 1900, the tide of the war appeared to have turned favorably for the British, with a succession of victories and relief of the siege of Mafeking (Arnstein, 2003; Packard, 1995). After Mafeking, the Queen had been cheered in a triumphal progress through London by crowds comparable in number to those who had celebrated her Diamond Jubilee in 1897. In April she was greeted by enthusiastic throngs during a highly successful visit to Dublin. Then, at the beginning of the summer, she was present for the christening at Windsor of a great-grandchild, the future Earl Mountbatten of Burma, son of her beloved granddaughter Princess Victoria of Hesse and the well-regarded Prince Louis of Battenberg. So satisfaction and contentment outweigh grief—for now.

p 1–2 17 August *"A tremendously hot day.—Breakfasted in the tent.—Heard again through Reuter the confirmation of the news that the allied troops had entered Pellin & had released the Legations, but there is still no official news.— Sat out & wrote & signed.—Georgie* came to wish me goodbye, May remaining*

---

* The Queen's grandson, Prince George of Wales, was the future King George V but at this time the Duke of York. The husband of Princess May, Prince George was known the family as "Georgie."

until the 20th.—After luncheon & resting, saw L^d [illegible] & talked a good deal about affairs & conversations he had had with Ld Salisbury,* who himself rather feels the fatigue of the work of the 2 offices.—Then out with Lenchen & May & read some interesting dispatches. Afterwards drove with them by Quarr Abbey. It was a fine, but very hot evening.—Emily A., M^r. Goschen^† (came for one night), Sir A. Bigge,^‡ Col:Carington & Ld E. Clinton^§ dined with us. Had a good deal of talk with M^r.Goschen, who thinks & hopes it is true that the Allies have entered Pellin. Talked a good deal about China. He spoke in the highest terms of Louis Battenberg, & said there was nobody like him.—"

The following Journal entry, dated the next day, 18 August, reflects the Queen's enjoyment of life and discriminating eye for beauty, as she visits her old friend the Empress Eugenie on an idyllic summer evening. Here, accomplished amateur artist that she once had been, Queen Victoria reaches for a fitting phrase to elevate her observations—"the sea as blue as turquoise & the air very pleasant.—" Her positive outlook is reinforced by promising new bulletins from the front. That her son Affie has died only a few weeks previously, on 30 July, does not for the moment detract from the buoyancy of these passages, although the loss has been crushing.

p 2–3 18 August *"It was overpoweringly hot.—Breakfasted out as usual, & then sat under the trees. Lenchen read to me as I wrote.—At ¼ p. 5 drove down to*

---

* Lord Salisbury (Robert Gasgoyne-Cecil, 3rd Marquess of Salisbury) was at the time both Prime Minister and Secretary of State for Foreign Affairs.

† George Joachim Goschen, later 1st Viscount Goschen, was First Lord of the Admiralty from 1895 to (October) 1900, and a confidante of Queen Victoria.

‡ Sir Arthur Bigge, later 1st Baron Stamfordham, was Private Secretary to Queen Victoria from 1895 to 1901, succeeding Sir Henry Ponsonby. He was subsequently Private Secretary to King George V for most of that king's reign.

§ Lord Edward William Pelham-Clinton was a British politician and one-time MP who held the post of Master of the Household to Queen Victoria from 1894 to 1901.

Trinity Pier with Lenchen & Beatrice, & paid a visit to the Empress Eugenie*
on board her yacht the 'Thistle,' which had been brought alongside the 'Alberta,'
so that I could walk on board. We took tea with her & sat a little while talking,
after which we went back to the 'Alberta,' & when the 'Thistle' had moved off, we
steamed off towards Yarmouth & back. It was a lovely evening, the sea as blue
as turquoise, & the air very pleasant.—There was again a report, & apparently
quite authentic, that the Allies had entered Pirie & that the Legations were quite
safe.—Ld Roberts† telegraphed that Christle‡ had arrived at Pretoria & was now
with him as his A.D.C. Emily A. & Mary H. dined.–"

The Queen has long had a sentimental and painterly appreciation of
natural beauty. From childhood and adolescence, and to a lesser extent
as she recovered from Prince Albert's death, she drew and painted in
several mediums, most successfully in watercolors. She was an enthusiastic
and talented, if undisciplined artist. Her pictures were frequently scenes
of Balmoral and the Highlands or the Solent off the Isle of Wight near
Osborne. In a letter sent 30 years before these Journal entries to a favorite
granddaughter, the then 7-year-old Princess Victoria of Hesse (28 April,
1870) (Hough, 1975, p. 1), she demonstrates the pleasure she derived from
natural beauty, in this case the summer primroses in her garden at Osborne.
(She characteristically signs off with her unique blend of homeliness and

---

    * The Empress Eugenie, wife of Napoleon III and Empress of France (1853–70), now widowed and living in exile, was much admired by Queen Victoria for her beauty and her dignity in adversity.

    † Frederick Roberts, 1st Baron and later 1st Earl of Kandahar, was Field Marshall of the British Army and Commander-in-Chief in the late Victorian era.

    ‡ Prince Christian Victor of Schleswig-Holstein, known as "Christle," was a grandson and great favorite of Queen Victoria. A soldier in the South African conflict, his safety was a worry to the Queen, as will become evident in later Journal entries [see additional footnote, Chapter 3].

self-deprecation—"ever your devoted old Grandmama"—which is then
contradicted by a dash of official hauteur—"Victoria R.I."):

Darling little Victoria,

...I wish you could see the thousands of beautiful primroses we have
here [at Osborne]! The grass and banks are covered with them & the
nightingales sing beautifully....

Ever your devoted old Grandmama
Victoria R.I.

Fifteen years after that letter, another one to the same recipient, the now
22-year-old Princess Victoria of Hesse, also demonstrates the Queen's
nostalgic expressions of awe and delight in the natural world. Here she
has been traveling in France (Maison Mottet, Aix les Bains, 3 April 1885)
(Hough, 1975, p. 73). Her closing is almost the same as the one composed
15 years earlier.

Darling Victoria,

...This afternoon in our drive we saw the snowy range of the Alps
–rising above the other high mountains, wh. was a pleasure to me as
I so delight in mountains & hills. You surely know those beautiful
lines of Byron's Poem of 'The Island'?

'He who first met the Highland's swelling blue
Will love each peak wh. shows a kindred face [sic]
Hail in each crag a friend's familiar face

And clasp the Mountain in his mind's embrace'

I always *feel that* in mountainous countries.

Ever your devoted old Grandmama
V.R.I.

As the daughter and mother of soldiers, Queen Victoria is always moved by "conspicuous acts of gallantry." Also, she frequently observes, and comments on, male beauty, as she does in the entry for 20 August.

p 4–5 20 August *"Very hot. We breakfasted under the cedar tree on the lane. After taking leave, May left for London.   Sat out, & dictated to Beatrice.   The Empress Eugenie came to luncheon, & immediately afterwards I gave the Victoria cross to Capt:Mouselle Jarves of the West York Reg^t—who came in on crutches. He was a fine looking young man & had been severely wounded at Terrace Hill on the Lugela, where he had performed conspicuous acts of gallantry...."*

No longer impatient with the Queen's seemingly endless, if increasingly *pro forma*, mourning for Albert, many of her subjects now commiserated with their again-sorrowing monarch after the death of her son Affie on 30 July. The letters of some of her ladies, lauding her artistic sensibilities and commiserating with the losses she has suffered, at times seem overwrought. Marie Mallet, keenly observant and probably the most sincerely loving of Queen Victoria's ladies-in-waiting, wrote on 4 August, almost two weeks before the first entry of the Journal's final volume:

We have just had a touching little Memorial Service [at Osborne, for Affie] in the Chapel here with beautiful prayers and heavenly

music…. The Queen bore up bravely…and I do not think there
was a dry eye in the congregation, not so much out of love for the
departed, but out of the deepest sympathy for the darling Queen
who seems called upon every day to bear some fresh sorrow. (Mallet,
1968, p. 204).

At this point we have seen the peak of the Queen's blithe spirits. It would
appear that she had been attempting to "hold on," enjoying the sensations
of summer at Osborne in her Journal entry of 18 August. But, now, in the
22 August entry, we hear the first statement, more than a hint, that all is
not in fact satisfactory: "—Did not feel well all day.—"

It would difficult to ignore a connection between her lack of well-being
and the recent death of Affie. Although she had been aware of Affie's illness,
his death had been a loss the Queen had not been anticipating, at least so
soon, and she refers on 22 August to its "suddenness." On the day of Affie's
death, 30 July 1900, she had written to Vicky (Ramm, 1990, p. 254):

I little thought when I wrote yesterday giving a bad account of our
beloved Affie that the end was so near…. We have been kept quite
in the dark and he, poor dear, in writing to poor dear Marie [Affie's
wife] never mentioned his health even though already some time
ago he was very ill…. It is hard at eighty-one to lose a third grown
up child in the prime of life….*

In this (22 August) Journal entry the Queen shows, for her, an unusual lack
of interest in the specific circumstances of the death of a member of her

---

* The Queen's children who had previously died were Princess Alice, Grand Duchess
of Hesse and by Rhine, who succumbed to diphtheria in Darmstadt in 1878; and Prince
Leopold, Duke of Albany, who died in Cannes, France, from the complications of hemophilia
after a fall in 1884.

family. More typical had been her reaction in 1897 when a distant relative, the Duchesse d'Alençon, had died in Paris in a charity bazaar fire. "It makes me *shudder*," she wrote after that tragic event, and later seemed to dwell on the fact that the only part of Duchesse's body that had been recovered was "the head" (Victoria, R.I., 1897). Now she merely alludes to Affie's having suffered from "different ailments for some time," although she well knew that he had died from advanced cancer of the throat and tongue. The shock of Affie's death is not only to his widow, "poor Marie," but, more typically for Queen Victoria, personalized to herself.

The intensity of the Queen's reaction to Affie's death was also quite different than her more matter-of-fact acceptance of the loss of another son, her youngest, Leopold (Duke of Albany) in 1884. Prince Leopold had enjoyed a closer relationship with his mother than her other sons, and had, to the chagrin of the Prince of Wales, been the only one of her children entrusted with regular access to state papers. But Leopold's death had come as no great surprise, as Leopold suffered from hemophilia, and a fatal accident, such as the one that occurred when he fell down a set of stairs, was practically fore-ordained.

The powerful emotional impact of Affie's death on the Queen was at odds with her comparatively harsh and critical view of him in life. Queen Victoria's attitude toward motherhood in general had been ambivalent and unsentimental; when young, her children had always been subordinated to her all-important role as Sovereign. From the birth of her first child the Queen had regarded pregnancy and motherhood as physically distasteful, if not repugnant, with a destructive effect on her womanly attractiveness and a distraction from the emotional and physical fulfillment of marriage. Furthermore, she never wholly enjoyed the presence of children, a statement that requires two qualifiers: First, she was not drawn to her *own* children when young, but warmed to them to varying degrees as they approached adulthood; and second, she was more openly affectionate with other people's children and with her grandchildren, especially Victoria of Hesse and Christian Victor of Schleswig-Holstein (Christle).

A touching letter to her ten-year-old granddaughter Princess Marie Louise of Schleswig-Holstein, Christle's sister, partially reproduced here, offers an interesting digression, revealing the sweet grandmotherly side of Queen Victoria's contradictory maternal character; it also concisely expresses the principles of proper comportment as she saw them (H.H. Princess Marie Louise, 1956, pp. 19–20):

Dear little Louise,

On this your tenth birthday I write to express my best wishes, praying that God may bless and protect you for many years and help to make you a good, truthful, affectionate little girl, dutiful and loving to Papa, Mama, and Grandmama, and kind and good to all around you. I hope you will like your watch and spend a happy birthday. Cousin Sophie [Queen of Greece] and Margaret Mossey [Princess Margaret of Prussia] send you much love....

Ever your loving Grandmama,
V.R.I.
Auntie Beatrice sends you her love.

Kindly and conventionally grandmotherly as the letter may be, one can find in it a source of her irritation with Affie, whose arrogant attitude with servants and courtiers violated the Victorian ideals she set out in the letter to young Marie Louise. So the Queen's direct progeny grew up at considerable physical and emotional remove from her, and were often the target of her criticism and scathing rebukes. Then, as adults, despite improving relations, Queen Victoria's children remained reluctant to contradict her in any way.

Affiie had apparently undergone a post-mortem absolution in Queen Victoria's eyes, nothing approaching the deification of Albert, but remarkable nonetheless, considering the extent of her previous irritation and disapproval of his behavior. It is also, of course, possible that the sad reaction to Affie's death here, and others later on, may have been emphasized by Princess Beatrice's editing of the Journal so as to favor the more engaging and attractive spectra of the Queen's emotional range. But whatever their authenticity, her expressions of grief are movingly expressed in the Journal; and the inconsistencies revealed in the Queen's delayed and then unexpectedly intense reaction to Affie's death suggest a contribution from her growing state of depression—the depression augmenting grief, and the grief augmenting depression. Although it is not yet apparent from her Journal entry for 22 August, the death of Affie will prove to be a turning point in Queen Victoria's life, effectively marking the beginning of her physical and emotional decline (Packard, 1998).

p 7 22 August *"Very showery morning.—It improved later, & I went for a turn.—Did not feel very well all day.—Rested & dozed after luncheon, which did me good.—Had tea in the breakfast tent, & then drove with Lenchen & Emily A.—When I came in, saw Sir Condie Stephen,* who has just come over from Coburg. He said how dreadful all had been, & how much he had felt it, & the suddenness of the end. He had seen dear Affie the day before he died & had thought him fearfully altered. Dr Florschutz had told him dear Affie had been suffering from different ailments for some time. The shock to poor dear Marie had been quite terrible, who had behaved so generously & kindly to everyone. Sir C.*

---

* Sir Condie Stephen was Private Secretary to Prince Alfred, Duke of Edinburgh and Duke of Coburg.

Stephen said little Charlie* had made an excellent impression, & spoke of the various arrangements which seem quite satisfactory. Emily A., Sir C. Stephen, Sir A. Bigge, Col:Carrington & Ld E. Clinton dined.–"

The conflict with the Boers in South Africa to which the Queen is referring in the next entry (23 August) was not her war, particularly, but she was the head of state, and as such felt keenly responsible. It was in her name that soldiers were dying. Casualty lists had always been distressing to her, and from this point on, these tragic lists will be important circumstantial factors in the gathering threads of her depression.

p 8–9 23 August *"A very showery morning, so that we could not breakfast out, but it cleared later & I went to Barton with Lenchen & Beatrice.—After luncheon & resting, saw Sir Condie Stephen again & looked through some of the photographs he brought here, which were painfully interesting.... The news from S. Africa continues much the same, repeated small fights, alas! costing many valuable lives.–"*

The warm summer days are now shortening. In nearly every Journal entry, Queen Victoria closely observes and comments on weather, but here, on 24 August, she is emphatic; it is still "fine," but she says that the days are shortening "very much." At the risk of overstatement, it is tempting, knowing what is to follow, to view this comment as prescient, a first suggestion that this is the beginning of the end of the Queen's life.

---

* "Little Charlie," also known as "Charlie Albany," was Prince Charles Edward, Duke of Albany, the son and heir of Queen Victoria's deceased son Prince Leopold. In 1900, at the age of 16, "Little Charlie" had been chosen—commanded, actually—by the Queen to succeed his late uncle Affie (Prince Alfred) as the reigning duke of Saxe-Coburg and Gotha. He was later vilified in England for having been a member of the Nazi Party and head of the German Red Cross in World War II.

With her prerogatives as Sovereign now considerably narrowed, the Queen views the comfort of soldiers as her personal province, beyond the reach of Government dictates. It had been her own idea, typically self-oriented but in this case a winning gesture, to send a chocolate bar stamped with her image to soldiers in the Veld for the previous Christmas (lest they forget for whom they have been fighting).

p 9–10 24 August *"A fine morning, & we breakfasted in the tent, after which we drove to Whippingham & placed a wreath in the Chapel…. On returning I sat in the tent, & Beatrice helped me to tear up letters, after which I took leave of Sir Condie Stephen, & gave him the 2nd class of the Victorian order, in recognition of his services to dear Affie & during all this trying time.—Had tea with Lenchen, Beatrice & Thora, & afterwards drove with the former & Maud Landsdowne, who is always so charming. It was a very fine enjoyable evening, but the days are shortening very much.—Saw Ld Landsdowne* about the war & army matters & found him very anxious to make the position of the soldiers as good as possible.—Emily A., the Landsdownes, Sir A. Bigge, Col:Carrington & Major E. Martin dined.–"*

On 26 August the birthday of the late Prince Consort ("this ever dear day") is experienced, as usual by the Queen, with bittersweet memories, but now with an acute dimension of sadness contributed by the death of Affie. Here again, the unpleasing aspects of Affie's character—his arrogance, his drinking—are now forgotten. She mourns her son not only for herself but also in absentia for the Prince Consort, as she feels certain he would have

---

* Henry Petty-Fitzmaurice, 5th Marquess of Landsdowne, Irish peer and British politician, was Viceroy of India from 1888 to 1894, then Secretary of State for War until October 1900. After that time, Prime Minister Lord Salisbury reorganized his cabinet, relinquished the post of Foreign Secretary which he had held himself along with the Prime Ministership, and bestowed it on Lord Landsdowne. Maud Landsdowne, wife of the Marquess, was much admired by the Queen.

done himself if he had been living. Affie's death has been a threshold event in the destruction of the Queen's once-superb resilience.

p 11 26 August *"This ever dear day* [the Prince Consort's birthday] *has returned again without my beloved Albert being with me, who on this day 81 years ago came into the world as a blessing to so many. Leaving an imperishable name behind him! I remember the happy day it used to be & preparing presents for him, which he would like! I thought much of the birthday speech at the dear lovely Rosenau in '45, when I so enjoyed being there & now his poor dear son of whom he was so proud, has breathed his last. Another birthday was spent 10 years later at St. Cloud, in the lovely place, now gone, when the Emperor & Empress, were so kind to us & dear Albert was not well. His last birthday of all he spent at the Vice Regal Lodge & we went to Killarney. All, all is engraven on my mind & in my heart!"–…Took tea under the cedar tree…where it was rather cold, then drove with Lenchen & Emily A. There was such a beautiful sunset.—Heard more favourable news from Ld Roberts. He had reached Belfast & had had a conference with Sir Redvers Buller* & Gen:French.–"*

Also on 26 August, Queen Victoria writes in a similar vein to her daughter the Empress Frederick ("Vicky")[†] in Germany (Ramm, 1990, p. 255). In this letter she is seeking to divert herself from the difficult present with happy memories of the past, and the result is as nostalgic as expected. At the same time she is unburdening herself to her eldest daughter, the one who had been, among the nine, the closest to Prince Albert. With Vicky, the

---

* Major-General Sir Redvers Buller was a popular soldier and important military strategist in the Second Boer War.

† Princess Victoria, the Princess Royal of Great Britain and Ireland, was the Queen's first child and one of those closest to her. By marriage she became Crown Princess Frederick of Prussia, then Empress (consort) of a newly united Germany. After the death of her husband Frederick III, she used the title "Empress Frederick" as the dowager, but throughout her life she was known in the family as "Vicky."

Queen could also share the experience of being a widow, about which she is referring when she laments the absence of "our dear ones once with us."

> This is a day which makes me think so particularly of you, darling child, and of former very bright happy days and all our dear ones once with us. They [memories] are very dear and cast a reflection of the past on the present very altered life. I have been thinking very much of that day which we spent at lovely St. Cloud, with its beautiful avenue and flags....

The Queen's departure from Osborne for Balmoral on 31 August adhered generally to her customary annual schedule of migration to and from her principal homes at Windsor, Osborne, and Balmoral, but this year (1900), she finds leaving Osborne to be especially wrenching. It is as if she felt she might never again see the much-loved island retreat where most of her children were raised, a home whose design indelibly bore the stamp of Prince Albert's influence (although Balmoral did as well). This was to be her last summer there. When she actually did return to Osborne for Christmas, as usual, she was in anything but her usual condition, being at that point in a much weakened and depressed state. It was at Osborne that she was to die on 22 January 1901.

p 17 31 August *"It was a most beautiful morning, everything looking so lovely, it makes one sad to go away.—Left the house, with Beatrice, Ena,* and Drino† at*

---

* Princess Victoria Eugenia of Battenberg, later Queen of Spain, was a daughter of Prince and Princess Henry (Beatrice) of Battenberg and a granddaughter of Queen Victoria. She was known in the family, and also publicly, by the last of her given names, "Ena."

† Prince Alexander of Battenberg, grandson of Queen Victoria, was known as "Drino." He was a son of Princess Beatrice and Prince Henry of Battenberg and a brother of Princess Ena.

6, with great regret, as I love Osborne more & more.... The train left Portsmouth at 8. Had some dinner soon after, & afterwards Beatrice read me some dispatches, & some interesting things out of the newspapers.–"

References

Arnstein, W.L. (2003). *Queen Victoria.* Palgrave Macmillan: New York, NY, p. 191.

Hibbert, C. (2000). *Queen Victoria: A personal history.* Da Capo Press: Cambridge, MA, p. 163.

Hough, R. (Ed.). (1975). *Advice to my grand-daughter: Letters from Queen Victoria to Princess Victoria of Hesse.* Simon & Schuster: New York, NY, pp. 1, 73.

Mallet, V. (Ed.). (1968). *Life with Queen Victoria: Marie Mallet's letters from court, 1887–1901.* Houghton Mifflin Company: Boston, MA, p. 204.

Packard, J.M. (1995). *Farewell in splendor: The passing of Queen Victoria and her age.* Dutton/Penguin Books USA: New York, NY, p. 9.

Packard, J.M. (1998). *Victoria's daughters.* St. Martin's Griffin: New York, NY, p. 299.

Pope-Hennessy, J. (1959). *Queen Mary.* George Allen & Unwin Limited: London, UK, p. 333.

H.H. Princess Marie Louise. (1956). *My memories of six reigns.* Evans Brothers Limited: London, UK, pp. 19–20.

Ramm, A. (Ed.). (1990). *Beloved & darling child: Last letters between Queen Victoria & her eldest daughter, 1896–1901.* Sutton Publishing: Stroud, UK, pp. 254, 255.

Victoria, R.I. (1897). *Letter from Queen Victoria to the Empress Frederick (Kronberg Archives), 5 May, 1897.*

Victoria, R.I., (1900). *Queen Victoria's Journal (Royal Archives), 17 August–31 August, 1900,* pp. 1–17.

3. Balmoral Castle from 1 September to 6 November, 1900: "…*a fresh link with the past gone!*"

On 1 September the Queen journeys to Balmoral, arriving "rather tired" despite having managed to get some sleep in the train. Inserting the qualifier "rather" is a frequent flourish of Queen Victoria's, used in her Journal and letter-writing when she did not wish to fully acknowledge that which she was actually experiencing, in this case, fatigue; otherwise, the Queen moved in a world of unqualified certitudes.

She writes here about the sympathy she has received over the death of Affie. As the Queen is confronted by new losses, the expressions and gestures of sympathy offered by others will be documented repeatedly in the Journal, from now throughout the rest of her life.

Of these exchanges Queen Victoria tends to record few of the actual words, but instead captures the essence of the emotion expressed to her. Here it is "sorrow & regret," which she finds moving, if not fully satisfying. In this regard, Marie Mallet (Mallet, 1968, p. 123) wrote to her husband Bernard in 1897: "We talked of people being sympathetic and the reverse and the Queen said, 'It makes the whole difference to me if I know people may be good and trust-worthy but if they lack sympathy I can never feel the same towards them.'"

Experiencing the sympathy of others is nothing new for Queen Victoria. It has long been a reliable, although ephemeral, source of comfort, one to which she has turned repeatedly in the past to refresh its effect; she often seemed to be deriving a form of pleasure from the self-pity that the sympathy of others reinforced. Although a serious depression is beginning to become established, it is probably best not to read this particular reaction—gratification derived from the commiseration of others—as evidence confirming her depression, since the Queen had persisted in portraying herself as the suffering widow long after her actual recovery from Albert's death. Similarly, the oppressive quiet, the "whispery" atmosphere she maintained in her homes, prevailed after Albert's death in times of recovery as well as mourning.

p 19 1 September *"Slept without waking.—Reached Perth after 9, where the Duke of Atholl received me.... Had luncheon in the train & reached Ballater at 2. It was very misty & showery driving here, but was fine in between.–...Went out about 6 with Harriet P.,* & called at Donald Stewart's & Arthur Grant's. Both spoke with much sorrow & regret of dear Affie.—Only the ladies dined.— Feeling rather tired.–"*

Upon arrival at Balmoral, the Queen is immediately reminded of, and now overwhelmed by, the loss of Affie, who had spent autumns in his youth and young manhood there. But her memories are again selective. In this entry she emphasizes the pleasures Affie had derived from the sport and dancing at Balmoral. But Affie, probably the most exasperating to her of her four sons, had been a peevish, confrontational personality. He had been a hard drinker, too, a circumstance which the Queen found worrying, and he had

---

* The Hon. Harriet Phipps was Personal Secretary to the Queen, charged with the responsibility for managing the Royal Household, but not State or Governmental affairs.

often been the subject of anxious discussions she had had with her principal physician, Sir James Reid.*

So Affie's Balmoral times had not, in fact, been altogether happy ones. The Queen, whose practice it was to behave more informally with servants in Scotland than at Osborne or Windsor, had frequently felt it necessary to upbraid Affie for his haughtiness with them. At one point she warned him sternly that she would not tolerate "naval discipline" in her own home (Weintraub, 1988). Above all, the Queen had been outraged by Affie's openly contemptuous attitude toward her special Scottish "friend," her servant John Brown, with whom he had had several memorable run-ins.

But on 2 September, in the aftermath of his death, all unpleasantness has now been forgotten, forgiven, or suppressed.

p 20 2 September *"Here I am again & what fresh sorrow has come upon me. How darling Affie loved the sport of all kinds here, how he used to enjoy the balls, danced so beautifully, shot so well, - & now, all, all is passed.... He first came here when he was only 4, after having been ill & it quite set him up again. But he never really was very strong.... Heard that Ld Roberts...had today issued proclamations...at Belfast announcing that the Transvaal would henceforth form part of my Dominions. Had tea at home, & then took a drive with Harriet P. & Doris V. It was bitterly cold but dry.—1,700 more of our prisoners have*

---

* Sir James Reid, Bt. was the Queen's greatly trusted personal resident physician. He will have a critically important role in the coming months. [See extensive footnote (Chapter 4)].

come into Sir R. Buller's camp.—Jane C., Harriet P., Doris V., Sir F. Edwards, Col:Davidson, & Fritz Ponsonby† dined.—"*

But now death is all around, inescapable. In the Queen's 3 September entry, death is suggested by her allusion to the flowers at Balmoral, dwarfed this year by a "cold wet summer" and finished off by an early frost. As often happens in the Journal, the tone of Queen Victoria's comments on nature, especially the weather, tends to be a projection of her own mental state; so her reports on nature or the weather are congruent with her mood and also with the tenor of events, the latter including her own losses and the ceaseless, unsettling accumulation of casualties in South Africa.

p 21 3 September *"A bright morning & not as cold as yesterday, but there were 5½ degrees of frost in the night, which has done much damage in the garden, where already the flowers have not come up as well as in former years, owing to the cold wet summer.—News keeps coming in of small fights, & taking of prisoners, ammunition, etc.—Only the Ladies to dinner...."*

In the past, her late summer and autumn sojourns at Balmoral have been reliably restorative for the Queen, but in 1900, again grieving, she finds it impossible to avoid the sights and images that stir sad memories and draw her attention back to her most recent loss; they are everywhere. For example, she is startled to encounter, on the grounds of Balmoral, the granite blocks she herself had ordered for Affie's tomb.

---

* Lady Jane Churchill, daughter of the 2nd Marquess of Conyngham, wife of the 2nd Baron Churchill, was one of the Queen's longest serving Ladies of the Bedchamber and a close friend and confidant for over 50 years. Her sudden death at Osborne on Christmas Day 1900 was a sorrowful shock to the Queen and preceded her own death by only a few weeks.

† Fritz Ponsonby (Sir Frederick Ponsonby, later 1st Lord Syonsby) was the son of the Queen's longtime Private Secretary, Sir Henry Ponsonby, and was himself Assistant Private Secretary to three monarchs: Queen Victoria, King Edward VII and King George V.

p 24–25 7 September *"It was very wet early, but soon cleared.–…Drove with Daisy to the Gen Gelder Shiel…. Drove home round by Boxman's Moss. As we came down the road, passed large fine blocks of granite, which I have had taken from our quarry, & are going to Aberdeen, to be made into a sarcophagus for dear Affie's tomb. I thought he would have liked the idea, of its coming from Balmoral itself, but it gave me quite a turn seeing it, & knowing what use it was going to be put to. A fine still evening, but very dull.—"*

On 10 September Queen Victoria reacts to the death of the physician of her son-in-law, Prince Henry of Battenberg, the husband of her youngest daughter, Beatrice. Prince Henry, known as "Liko,"* had died of malaria in 1896 aboard a ship returning him home from serving in Africa, and it had been Dr. Hilliard who had taken care of him, "nursing him so tenderly," albeit unsuccessfully. Queen Victoria often memorialized not only the person most directly mourned, but also those who knew, loved or assisted him. Her grief would encompass the concentric personal circle of the deceased.

In what has by now declared itself to be an unrelenting season of loss for the Queen, the death of Dr. Hilliard represented yet another "fresh link with the past gone." The phrase "fresh link with the past" is one of several Victorian variations on the same theme which can be found throughout the Queen's Journal and letters after Prince Albert's death in 1861. Similar words had been used by the Princess of Wales after the death of her elder son Prince Albert Victor in 1891, in her case adding that the Prince's death, her own "fresh link with the past," had brought her "one step closer to Heaven" (HSH Princess Victoria Mary, 1892).

---

* Prince Henry of Battenberg, a morganatic descendant of the Grand Ducal House of Hesse and by Rhine, was known from childhood as "Liko." Prince Henry married Princess Beatrice, the Queen's youngest daughter, in 1885. Liko was a great favorite of the Queen, who reluctantly allowed him to volunteer for the Ashanti expedition in West Africa in 1895. He died of malaria on the ship returning him home in January 1896.

p 28–29 10 September *"Was greatly grieved & shocked to hear that excellent Dʳ Hilliard, (who was with Liko all through his fatal illness, going down with him to Cape Coast Castle, nursing him so tenderly, & in whose arms he had died on board the 'Blaude') was dangerously wounded at DooruKop & succumbed to his wounds. It was quite a shock hearing this, & Beatrice was much upset by the news. It seemed a fresh link with the past gone!"*

The next day, 11 September, the weather has improved, and so, temporarily, have the Queen's spirits. In the Journal entry for this day, her appreciation of natural beauty, particularly of the Deeside landscapes and sunsets, is much in evidence. Also, Princess May, a person particularly loved and admired by Queen Victoria, is a dependably supportive presence, and on this occasion she contributes her reassuring cheerfulness and friendliness. Perhaps in the company of May, herself a future Queen Consort, Victoria is able to reach beyond her doubts about her direct heir and can feel reassured about the stability of the monarchy in the third generation. May is joined on this occasion by Princess Irene of Hesse, another amiable, if unexciting person. The Queen carries on with her drives, and she remains in a comparatively cheerful frame of mind for the next forty-eight hours, through 13 September.

But even on 11 September, a mostly satisfactory day, there is still a plaintive aspect to the Queen's account; her pleasure is not in the present, but in reminiscence, savoring memories of places associated with a happier past. On this day she drives from Balmoral Castle to take tea at Altuaghuitasach, "which I had not done for a long time."

Although there is no such comment by the Queen, Princess Beatrice, in contrast to May, had at this time begun to show signs of weariness in her service to her mother. According to Marie Mallet, Beatrice was becoming "dreadfully self-absorbed and unsympathetic" (Mallet, 1968, p. 203). Princess Beatrice's attitude was felt by many close to the Queen to also have potentially adverse political implications, since with the Queen's failing vision, it was Beatrice alone who was entrusted to read official documents and memoranda to her; and Beatrice, fatigued or resentful or simply bored, often skipped over critical Foreign Office and other dispatches. In this way she compounded the impact of her mother's poor vision and incipient decline in memory, and left the Queen, never a policy-maker but still as monarch a constitutionally indispensable lever in the mechanics of government, in the dark about key events (Pope-Hennessy, 1959, p. 345).

p 29 11 September *"A very fine day.—Out with Beatrice & gave away presents, May & Irene* joining us on the way.—In the afternoon, which was beautiful, drove with Beatrice & May to Altuaghuitasach, where we took tea, which I had not done for a long time. There was a most beautiful sunset.—Jane C., Ld Cross,[†] Sir H. Ewart, Herr von Leckendorff, & Col:Davidson dined.—"*

p 29–30 12 September *"... To my joy able to breakfast in the Cottage, as it was a beautiful hot day. Took a turn, & then sat at the Cottage till past 1.—"*

p 30–31 13 September *"Another most splendid day.—Breakfasted outside, near the Cottage, where it was delightful.... Took a short turn, & then sat out & wrote.—Drove in the afternoon with Irene & May to the Glassalt, where we met the rest of the family, some of whom had been up Lachnagar, & we had tea together. It was a beautiful evening.... Heard that Kruger had gone to Lorenzo Marquez, intending to embark for Holland, & taking a deal of money*

---

* Princess Irene of Hesse was a sister of Princess Louis of Battenberg (née Victoria of Hesse) and also of the Tsarina Alexandra of Russia (née Alix of Hesse). Irene, Victoria and Alix were daughters of Princess Alice, Grand Duchess of Hesse and by Rhine, the Queen's third child.

† Richard Assheton Cross, 1st Viscount Cross, was a British political figure who held the office of Home Secretary between the years of 1874 and 1880 and again between 1885 and 1886. Later he became Lord Privy Seal, a largely ceremonial post.

with him. But the fighting still continues. There was also rather pressing news from China.—"

It is on 17 September at Balmoral that the Queen delivers the first serious, somewhat cryptic, and definitely sudden warning that she has not been feeling well. Although previously unmentioned, she refers to this development as already long established, her loss of appetite having been "a great trouble for some time past." The fact that anorexia was the first symptom to be identified by the Queen neither confirms nor excludes a depressive etiology, but the absence of other explanations to account for the change in appetite must be considered to be consistent with depression.

p 34 17 September "—*Drove with Irene & May to the Birkhall approach, where we took our tea, which for me consists of arraroot & milk. I have not been feeling very well these last days, & can eat very little. This has been a great trouble for some time past.—Jane C., Ld Cromer,* Col:Davidson & M^r. Keppel dined.—"*

On 19 September the Queen rallies to address troops of the West African Frontier Force outside the Castle. Despite the rather condescending reference ("The Jarubas…are very quiet hard working people when properly looked after…."), this is the kind of event favored by Queen Victoria and for which she has always been at her best; her matchless sense of occasion does not fail her now. She is seen to be taking very seriously her role as the representative embodiment of the Empire and the values for which its soldiers must risk their lives. She offers carefully worded messages of encouragement and pride in her Indian army, worthy, as the worshipful Marie Mallet suggested, of Queen Elizabeth addressing her sailors before

---

* Evelyn Baring, 1st Earl of Cromer, served as Counsel-General in Egypt from 1883 to 1907.

they met the Spanish Armada. In her strikingly clear and young-sounding voice the Queen expresses her gratitude to the Madrasses and Jarubas. She is outraged to hear of an incident in which the Boers entrapped a party of the 13th Hussars: "It is too monstrous for words."

p 35–37 19 September *"Cold rather damp morning…. At 12 drove with Beatrice & May …to inspect a Detachment of Troops…who form part of the West African Frontier Force. The Jarubas are recruits from Upper Guinea… & are very quiet hard working people when properly looked after…. They all wore Khaki, the Madrasses having turbans of the same colour & the Jarubas red skull caps with tassels, the latter having bare feet. After the Royal Salute, filing past & forming up in line, I addressed the following words to the men: 'I am very pleased to see you here. I am very proud of my Indian Army & watched with the greatest interest the excellent work they have been doing, not only in Africa, but also in China….' In a telegram from Ld Roberts about different small engagements… he mentions that on the 15th, a party of 13th Hussars patrolling…were invited …into a farm over which a white flag was flying, & offered some milk & bread, whereupon, as they were leaving the farm, they were fired upon…. It is too monstrous for words—…."*

The Queen closely follows the news from South Africa and laments the losses ("…alas! always fresh lives lost!—"), even when the overall report, as on 24 September, is "satisfactory." The Queen genuinely admires Lord Roberts, who himself had lost a son in the conflict. Lord Roberts has been proposed as the next Commander in Chief, but the Queen had long harbored the hope that her son Arthur* would replace her cousin the Duke of Cambridge in that position. These frustrated hopes for Arthur, ambitions

---

* Prince Arthur, the Duke of Connaught, was the seventh child and third son of Queen Victoria and Prince Albert. Princess Louise of Prussia, known by the diminutive "Louischen," was Arthur's wife.

that had been beyond her power as Sovereign to influence, may have been a source of the "many questions it [Lord Roberts's promotion] entails" (25 September).

p 40–41 24 September *"A bright morning.—Went out with Lenchen, Beatrice, Arthur, & Daisy. Arthur & Louischen had arrived, just as we were finishing breakfast. Both seemed well, & delighted with their stay in the Tyrol.... Bertie*** arrived at ½ p. 6 & sat with me some little while.—Satisfactory news coming in, only alas! always fresh lives lost!—Jane C., Ld Jarves, Sir F Edwards, & Capt:Seymour Fortescue dined with us. The latter, who had been attached to Ld Roberts's staff, lost a brother in S. Africa.–"*

p 41 25 September *"...Bertie & Arthur came to my room & we had a long talk about the proposal to make Ld Roberts Commander in Chief & the many questions it entails...."*

On 29 September the Queen refers to the ordeal in Germany of her daughter Vicky, the Empress Frederick, who has advanced breast cancer with spinal metastases. The pain in her spine had become unspeakable, and screams emanated periodically from her room. Vicky's suffering was being made only intermittently bearable with infrequent and inexplicably meagre injections of morphine (Packard, 1998). For what reason this dosing of crucial painkillers was so inadequate is not known, but it can be seen as an appalling parallel to the hostility and suspicion with which the Dowager Empress was regarded in Germany—not least by her own son, the mercurial Kaiser, who treated her with contempt and derision.

---

* Albert Edward, Prince of Wales, later King Edward VII, was known in the family as "Bertie."

p 43 29 September *"Dear Vicky's engagement day, which is a sad contrast to her present suffering state.—A dull, though less cold day.—Out rather late with Beatrice & Louie.–"**

Meanwhile, the Queen continues, as always, to memorialize the losses of those close to her by mentioning specific birthdays and other anniversaries. This grim list is growing ever longer. On 5 October it is the late Liko Battenberg's birthday. Her original opposition to Liko's marriage to Beatrice, indeed her stubborn reluctance to allow Beatrice to marry at all, are now apparently forgotten.

The 5 October entry also alludes to the Queen's convictions on human rights, sentiments not normally associated with her 19th-century Imperialist mindset. Here she applauds the release of Moroccan prisoners by that country's young Emperor. This is not the first such expression of humanitarian concern by Queen Victoria. In 1894, Her Majesty had called out as a "disgrace to France" the antisemitism that lay behind the unjust conviction for treason of Captain Alfred Dreyfus.

p 48–49 5 October *"This was dear Liko's birthday. How he is ever missed!—A nice bright morning though there had been showers.—Before going out saw Sir A. Nicholson, who presented me with a letter from the Emperor of Morocco. I told him to say everything kind & civil to the Emperor, who is only 19 & that I was so glad to hear he had released so many people from prison. I hoped he would continue in this course of humanity.... The letter was to ask me to define his frontier, which*

---

* Princess Francisca Josepha of Schleswig-Holstein (1872–1956), known by her preferred name, Princess Marie Louise ("Louie" to her family), lived into the reign of Queen Elizabeth II. A kindly, modest and charitable woman, although occasionally tipsy from drink in her later years, she initiated the project of creating an accurately detailed miniature dollhouse for Queen Mary. She published an autobiographical account in 1956: *My Memories of Six Reigns*, London, Evans Brothers Limited.

it is rather difficult for me to promise to do.–...It was a fine afternoon.—Only a family dinner, the Ladies joining us afterwards, & the Band played a charming selection of pieces.–"

Queen Victoria has been making concerted attempts to function, thus far with success, but she is being confronted with an onslaught of disquieting personal tidings. On 9 October, Vicky's condition has taken a worrying turn, although the Queen's very worst fears are not realized. However, she then moves on to a reference to the death of her young great-grandson in Darmstadt, both of whose parents, the Grand Duke and Grand Duchess of Hesse and by Rhine, "Ernie" and "Ducky," are her grandchildren.*

p 52 9 October *"A dull, but mild morning.... Beatrice came in with a telegram from Mossy saying darling Vicky had had a change for the worse...& heart failure. Was dreadfully distressed & upset, for it came as a great shock. Though we had been very unhappy & anxious lately to hear of her great sufferings, we were always told there was no danger. Lenchen decided at once to start for Germany.... Could think of nothing else & felt very wretched, as did we all.... After dinner a telegram arrived from the Doctor & Sir J. Reid, saying dear Vicky's heart failure had passed off, for which I thank God. Felt all the same very sad & anxious and L^y Georgina Buchanan both said how broken hearted Ernie & Ducky had been at the loss of their little boy, & that the people at Darmstadt had shown much feeling about it... ."*

On 10, 11, and also on 16 October, the Queen tries to convince herself that Vicky has been improving, and for now she does not question the unrealistic accounts she is given. Momentarily reassured, she finds sufficient energy to

---

* Prince Ernest Louis ("Ernie"), Grand Duke of Hesse and by Rhine, was the son of Princess Alice. Prince Ernest's first wife was Princess Victoria Melita of Edinburgh and Coburg ("Ducky"), a daughter of Prince Alfred.

consider on 16 and 17 October the multiple changes in the Cabinet that are being proposed, and then on 18 October, matters concerning Australia.

p 54 10 October *"...Drove with Harriet & Sylvia E. to Braemar & back.— Heard again that Vicky was improving & gaining strength.—A Ladies dinner & the Band played afterwards. Emily Ampthill has replaced Annie Roxburghe* today.–"*

p 54 11 October *"...had another satisfactory account of Vicky. Her strength is well maintained and she takes more food. Lenchen has put off her journey for the present.–"*

p 57 16 October *"A very beautiful day, after 11 degrees of frost, but very cold.—A good account of dear Vicky & the Doctor says there is no longer any danger.–... Saw Sir A. Bigge about all the changes in the Cabinet, owing principally to M*^{r}*. Goschen having resigned & also L*^{d}* Landsdowne intending to do so. There is a possibility of L*^{d}* Salisbury giving up the Foreign Office, on account of the work being too great, though he would still have the entire supervision of it* [as Prime Minister]. *Afterwards saw L*^{d}* Clarendon,*[†] *who seems very anxious to do everything he can in his new office...."*

p 59 17 October *"...I saw M*^{r}*. Akers Douglas & had a long talk with him about the various impending changes in the Cabinet, the possibilities, the qualities of the different people & the very great difficulties in deciding for the rest, the principal one of all being whether L*^{d}* Salisbury should continue to hold the 2 offices, the work being evidently too much for his health. On the other hand no one could be*

---

* Anne, Duchess of Roxburghe, was a Lady of the Bedchamber to Queen Victoria from 1897 to 1901.

† Edward Hyde Villiers, 5th Earl of Clarendon, was ADC to Queen Victoria in the last years of her reign.

as good for the Foreign Office as himself, but of course his life is most valuable for the country. But whatever is decided upon, he would naturally have to superintend everything in the office as Prime Minister. I will not write more about these changes at present, nor of course of the Court appointments which will have to be rearranged, on account of the death of some of the members, & the appointment of others to new posts.—Emily A., Sylvia E., Bessie B., M^r. Akers Douglas, M^r. Fitzroy (Clerk of the Council), Sir A. Bigge & Gen:Clark dined.–"

p 60 18 October *"A fine morning.—Out with Beatrice & Thora before holding a Council to arrange some business in connection with the Commonwealth of Australia for the further Prorogation of Parliament...."*

On 19 October appears one of the Queen's first complaints of physical distress, in this entry not specific, but conveying a general sense of malaise. Also, in this entry, and increasingly over the succeeding months, Queen Victoria chooses the starkest of terms, oppressive and heavy with feeling, congruent with her own darkening mood, to describe the shortening days and autumnal weather. Then, in a second entry for same date, she bemoans the "sad & useless loss of life" in South Africa. So it was "dark and dismal" on 19 October from every point of view.

She begins the next day determined to regain her footing, even has a new novel read aloud to her. But with a timing almost cruel, now that she has admitted to herself that she is "unwell," the Queen is confronted with more bad news from the front in South Africa on the 22nd. This time it is personal. She now learns that her soldier-grandson Prince Christian Victor of Schleswig-Holstein, Lenchen's son and always known as "Christle,"* has contracted enteric fever, i.e., malaria.

---

* Prince Christian Victor of Schleswig-Holstein ("Christle") was a son of Prince Christian of Schleswig-Holstein and Princess Christian (Princess Helena). The now-33-year-old soldier had already fought in the Sudan under Lord Kitchener and served with

This is ominous indeed. For reasons that remain obscure, Christle had been, from almost the moment of his birth, a great favorite of Queen Victoria. In a letter to the Crown Princess Frederick on 2 June 1867, the infant Princess Victoria Mary of Teck (the future Queen consort and daughter of Princess Mary Adelaide of Cambridge, whom Victoria would later come to so love and admire), is compared unfavorably by the Queen to the infant Christle , who had been born six weeks earlier: "Mary T[eck]* is going on perfectly well & it is a very fine child. However nothing can beat Lenchen's Boy—who one really sees grow *daily*—He is a splendid fellow" (Pope-Hennessy, 1959, p. 24).

p 59 19 October *"The morning was fair.—Was not feeling well all day.—Went with Beatrice and Thora as far as the village.—In the afternoon drove with the latter & Beatrice. It was very dark & dismal.–"*

p 61 19 October *"Distressing fighting goes on in S. Africa, & sad & useless loss of life. Sir Redvers Buller is leaving Cape Town for England, next week.–"*

p 61 20 October *"A fair morning…. After tea looked through some letters with Beatrice, & then Harriet P. read to me out of that interesting novel 'Under the Red Robe'.–"*

p 63 22 October *"A very dull dark day.—Heard to our great concern that Christle has enteric fever at Pretoria…."*

---

his uncle by marriage, the ill-fated Prince Henry of Battenberg, in the Ashanti expedition. Now, having fought in South Africa in the 60th King's Royal Rifles, for which duty he was widely respected, Christle contracted malaria three weeks before he was to return home to England (Packard, 1998).

* Princess Mary Adelaide of Cambridge, Duchess of Teck.

The message from Pretoria about Prince Christle's illness is concerning if not yet alarming, but on 23 October, the Queen, perhaps in search of distractions, is able to redirect herself to state affairs. On 23 October she composes what is probably the most businesslike entry in the final volume of the Journal, an account that is filled with meticulous strategic thinking (including her disdain for certain, presumably liberal, "objectionable measures") and insightful assessments of current political figures. If the Queen had incipient cognitive impairment, it was not evident at this moment.

Queen Victoria had been well aware that holding both the Prime Ministership and the Foreign Office might overtax her aging friend, Lord Salisbury. This concern has now been borne out, and the Foreign Office has been given over to Lord Landsdowne, with Lord Salisbury remaining as Prime Minister and also assuming the ceremonial post of Lord Privy Seal. The Queen has had a long and trusting relationship with the staunchly conservative Salisbury, a paragon of the nation's dwindling landed aristocracy. While accepting that Lord Salisbury would inevitably have to relinquish the Foreign Office, she deplores the change.

Marie Mallet comments on this turn of events in a letter written later (3 November) to her husband Bernard from Balmoral (Mallet, 1968, p. 214). The facetious remark attributed to Lord Salisbury about many more Ambassadorial afternoons shortening his life—depicting boredom as sufficient to cause death—was apparently conveyed by the Queen to Marie, but may have represented Marie's own embellishment, as sarcasm was not the kind of humor that the Queen would have been likely to repeat. Marie writes:

> I drove with the Queen this afternoon and she said Lord Lansdowne would not act in any way without Lord Salisbury, in fact he is to be a sort of 'dummy' to do the entertaining and tiresome interviews with Ambassadors and not to have any power. Lord Salisbury told the

Queen that many more Ambassadorial afternoons would certainly
shorten his life.

Marie's true feelings on the matter were expressed flippantly the day before,
in her letter of 2 November:

> It is quite evident that Lord Salisbury has 'thrown up the sponge.'
> It is comic to think of him in Lord Cross's place [Lord Privy Seal, a
> sinecure without meaningful power], while that poor old dodderer
> is plucking his beard and reviling the Government.

p 63–67 23 October *"A dull morning & a very dreary day.–…Saw Ld Salisbury…
had a great deal of discussion on all the various subjects of importance in the coming
changes in the Cabinet. The first & most important one is, that he himself feels he
ought __not__ to continue to hold both offices, as it is too much for his health. Contrary
to my expectation he was quite ready to do & propose this. The work would not be
too much for him if there was no important political crisis, but if that arose, he could
not undertake it, but he intended taking the Privy Seal himself, as he must have
an office. This would entail the retirement of Ld Cross, which we both regretted, but
felt would be as well, as he has aged much of late & did not like his present office. L^d
Salisbury thought the only person fitted to take the Foreign Seals was Ld Lansdowne,
but I said it ought to be under the strict understanding that he should be entirely
under Ld Salisbury's personal supervision…& that no telegrams or dispatches should
be sent without first being submitted to him. Then came the two very important
offices of the Admiralty & War Office. Ld Salisbury suggested that his son-in-law
Ld Selbourne should be appointed for the former. He is very able & has been lately
Under Secretary for the Colonies. To this I assented. As for the War Office, he felt,
taking it all around, M^r. Broderick would be the best person. Since having him as
Under Secretary for Foreign Affairs, he thought well of him. He was a good speaker
& worker & not connected with any of the objectionable measures. Ld Salisbury*

thought the Duke of Bedford would be a good Under Secretary as he would be able to speak for the Army in the House of Lords & is said to be very able. It was intended that Matthew White White [sic] Ridley should retire.... Many other subjects were touched upon; social & others, in all of which he showed, as usual great wisdom...."

Her ability to focus intermittently on the minutiae of political affairs and personalities belies the severity of the Queen's decline. Marie Mallet had gone off service at Osborne in August, then rejoined the Royal Household at Balmoral in October for her 12th term in waiting, two days after the first report of Christle's illness had reached the Queen. After barely two months away, Marie is shocked at the appalling changes in Queen Victoria's appearance (Mallet, 1968, p. 207). She rightly points to the Queen's facial expression as the key to her emotional state: "The Queen is growing very old and feeble, and each time I see the change, even since August. She has grown so thin and there is a distressing look of pain and weariness on her face; it makes me very sad."

Over the next few days, anxiety over Christle's condition mounts steadily. On 25 October, Marie (Mallet, 1968, p. 210) writes: "Princess Thora is awfully anxious about her brother. Lord Roberts wires he is seriously ill but there are no complications and he has the best of nurses and doctors."

Marie signs off on 25 October with the following sad but prescient comment: "It seems as if the poor darling Queen is never again to be free from anxiety."

In a similar vein, on 27 October, Marie views the Queen's worry about the deteriorating condition of the Empress Frederick as compounding the concern about Christle. The tension at Balmoral is now something terrible, with the principals endlessly turning over shreds of information for any sign of hope for Christle. Marie writes (Mallet, 1968, p. 211):

We live in a constant state of anxiety about Prince Christle and I really think the sudden telegrams add to the trial…as each one arrives…all the shades and symptoms are discussed, today the account is certainly serious, pneumonia and other complications but I have a strong feeling that he will pull through and come safely home. Still there must be awful suspense for another ten days at the very least and it is so bad for the Queen in addition to the worse anxiety about the Empress Frederick…. The dear little Queen makes heroic efforts to be cheerful but her face in repose is terribly sad….

Here again the astute Marie appreciates that emotional state is most directly to be gleaned from facial expression.

Then, on 29 October, comes the news that all at Balmoral had been dreading: Christle has succumbed to malaria. Well before Christle's death, Marie Mallet, referring to the death of Beatrice's husband, Liko Battenberg, in 1895 and to the more recent death of Affie on 31 July, 1900, wrote (Mallet, 1968, p. 200): "We seem to have shock after shock and everything is so sad I hardly know what to do or what to say." Once again, the Queen's life has been defined by grief. Now it can be said that if Affie's death had been a turning point in Her Majesty's physical and emotional decline, Christle's is to become the decisive blow.

The Queen's Journal entry for 29 October closes with the words "felt too upset to go out." This deceptively casual remark is actually very telling. For Queen Victoria, whose only "exercise" and escape from her closed-in women's world has been to take undemanding daily drives around the grounds of Windsor, Osborne or Balmoral, the fact that she was unable to gather the strength or will to "go out" underscores the intensity of her grief.

p 71–72 29 October *"Almost directly after I went upstairs [after luncheon], Thora* came in & in a faltering voice said 'He is gone.' I could not believe it, it seemed too dreadful & heartbreaking, this dear & excellent, gallant Boy, beloved by all, such a good, as well as brave & capable, officer, gone! To think he had gone through the Indian campaign, Ashanti, (where our beloved Liko was taken), the Sudan, going down in his ship & again in S. Africa had passed through endless hardships, & dangers, without being ill, or getting a scratch, —to fall a victim to this horrid fever, just on the eve of his return home, —oh! it is really too piteous. It brings back so vividly to my mind dear Liko's loss, dying of African fever, away from his dear ones. I am miserable in thinking of poor dear Lenchen, who so worshipped this son & poor Thora, so dear and so courageous, trying to comfort me by saying so sweetly she knew 'he was happy.'...Again & again the terrible thought of this fresh blow & irreparable loss, brought tears to my eyes. Poor dear Lenchen, poor Christian, who is abroad & loved this son so dearly! A wet afternoon & felt too upset to go out.—"*

The next day, 30 October, the heartbroken Queen reaches out to Vicky (Ramm, 1990, p. 257):

> ...I cannot write but a few words as we are in such distress about dear Christle's loss. It is too terribly sad to have gone through such hardships and dangers and not far from his return home to get that awful illness and be lost when all thought him safe. He had, alas, malarial and enteric fever. We hoped to the last. Poor dear Lenchen

---

* "Thora" was the name used in the family for Princess Helena Victoria of Schleswig-Holstein, a daughter of Prince and Princess Christian and sister of "Christle." Thora was a favorite granddaughter of Queen Victoria and was entrusted to take dictation for many of the Queen's Journal entries during the last year of Her Majesty's life [see footnotes on Prince Christian Victor of Schleswig-Holstein].

bears up wonderfully; so too does poor dear Thora who leaves for Cumberland Lodge today....

In a letter to her husband also dated 30 October, Marie refers to what is now the utter devastation at Balmoral and her worry about its effects on the Queen (Mallet, 1968, p. 211). "Words fail me to describe the pall of sorrow that hangs over this house, the Queen is quite exhausted by her grief... dreadfully shaken and upset and as she was not at her best before this shock you may imagine how anxious we feel about her health."

A few days later, on 2 November (Mallet, 1968, p. 213), Marie searches for a sign of determination, a will to survive and to carry on with her duties, in the Queen's otherwise sad countenance:

We remain in the same melancholy state here...gloomy evenings, silence only broken by the receipt of consoling telegrams in divers tongues and by the replies sent to them. The Queen...does her best to keep up, but the effort is very great and cannot be good for her. The curious thing is that she said to me, 'After the Prince Consort's death I wished to die, but *now* I wish to live and do what I can for my country and those I love.'

Despite these brave words, the Journal entries for 3 and 4 November mark the beginning of a bleak new baseline level of functioning for Queen Victoria. From this point, debilitating insomnia and its natural consequence, daytime fatigue, will be the rule rather than the exception. The Queen's feeble appetite also continues to worsen. Although Her Majesty has had symptoms of mood disorder for some time, there can be no doubt that she is now, in the aftermath of Christle's death, experiencing a significant episode of depression.

On 3 November the first anxiously anticipated contact with Lenchen, mother of Prince Christle, is mentioned. It helps, slightly perhaps, for the Queen to think of the place where Christle had died as a *'holy land.'* He is now to be included in her growing hagiography of the dead.

The Queen's symptoms are also linked—projected upon—the weather. This reflects the latest step in a recent change, since under the influence of one of her early physicians, Sir James Clark, the Queen had been for many years an enthusiastic advocate of the supposed health-promoting properties of cold weather. Now her descriptions of the chilly dampness exude only misery: "dreadfully dark," and "a most dreadful day, so very dark and wet and foggy."

p 79 3 November *"I had a very bad night, & could hardly get any sleep. Felt in consequence very wretched all day.—Had my first letter from poor Lenchen, very resigned but quite brokenhearted, also a nice one from Louise,* who has been twice to Cumberland Lodge & is very kind. In the afternoon drove with Edith L and Marie M.* [Mallet]. *It was dreadfully dark.–"*

p 80–81 4 November *"A most dreadful day, so very dark and wet and foggy.— Service at 11, performed by D^r McGregor. There were some fine passages in his sermon & beautiful allusions to dear Christle. In speaking of the many who had fallen in S. Africa & were resting there, he said it had become 'a holy land.' Saw D^r McGregor after tea who was very kind & full of sympathy.... My appetite is as bad as ever & has got much worse the last few days.–"*

Others, not only Marie Mallet, have observed changes in Queen Victoria's physical appearance and demeanor. When he arrived in Scotland early in

---

* Princess Louise, Marchioness of Lorne (later Duchess of Argyll), was the Queen's fourth daughter and sixth child.

November to take up his duties as Minister-in-Attendance, Lord James of Hereford was shocked at the change in the Queen's appearance from when he had last seen her in the summer, only a few months earlier: "The Queen had lost much flesh, and had shrunk so as to appear about one-half of the person she had been. Her spirits, too, had left her...." (Weintraub, 1988, p. 627).

On 5 and 6 November, the Queen's gloom deepens in concert with the darkening days and the reports of reversals in South Africa. Her appetite is now non-existent, and as she leaves Balmoral, for what is to be the last time, on 6 November, it is clear that this year's sojourn in the Scottish highlands has been anything but restorative for her.

At this point the Munshi ("teacher"), Hafiz Mohammed Abdul Karim, the Queen's Muslim servant and tutor of Urdu, returns after a visit to his native India to rejoin the Royal Household at Windsor. The Munshi has been a cherished confidant and someone to whom Queen Victoria has been closely drawn since his arrival in Britain in 1883. The objections, contempt and resentment of her children and Household, who considered him a brazen imposter, had served only to increase the Queen's resolve in creating for him a unique protected status. In some ways, the Munshi occupied a position with privileges similar to those granted to Her Majesty's Scottish ghillie John Brown in the aftermath of Albert's death. But now the Munshi's arrival goes unmentioned in the Journal, representing either another sign of the Queen's decline or a post-mortem edit of Princess Beatrice, who like the rest of the family, would have been keen to expunge any written evidence of what she and other family members considered to have been an inappropriate, if not scandalous, relationship.

p 81 5 November *"News of more fighting & more treachery. It is really dreadful & most distressing.... Felt very poorly & wretched, as I have done all the last days. My appetite is completely gone & I have great difficulty eating anything.–"*

p 82 6 November *"The day was dreadfully dark and foggy.... Left Balmoral at ½ p 2 driving to the station with Beatrice, Ena and Edith Lytton. It was wretchedly gloomy & dark. Had some coffee after Aberdeen. Got out for dinner at Perth but could, as usual eat next to nothing. Marie M. came into my saloon & remained until Carstairs. She read to me out of the papers.—"*

References

Mallet, V. (Ed.). (1968). *Life with Queen Victoria: Marie Mallet's letters from court, 1887–1901*. Houghton Mifflin Company: Boston, MA, pp. 123, 200, 203, 207, 210, 211, 213, 214

Packard, J.M. (1998). *Victoria's daughters*. St. Martin's Griffin: New York, NY, pp. 300, 307.

Pope-Hennessy, J. (1959). *Queen Mary*. George Allen & Unwin Limited: London, UK, pp. 24, 345.

HSH Princess Victoria Mary. (1892). *Letter from Princess Victoria Mary (May) of Teck to Miss Emily Alcock (Royal Archives), January 1892*.

Ramm, A. (Ed.). (1990). *Beloved & darling child: Last letters between Queen Victoria & her eldest daughter, 1896–1901*. Sutton Publishing: Stroud, UK, p. 257.

Victoria, R.I. (1900). *Queen Victoria's Journal (Royal Archives), 1 September–6 November, 1900*, pp. 18–82.

Weintraub, S. (1988). *Victoria: An intimate biography*. Truman Talley Books/ E.P. Dutton: New York, NY, pp. 377, 627.

4. Windsor Castle from 7 November to 17 December, 1900: *"Pain is in residence."* From *How It All Began* by Penelope Lively. Viking Press, New York, NY, 2011.

Arriving at Windsor on 7 November the Queen must contend with a much-dreaded reunion. She is to confront, face-to-face, for the first time since Christle's death, his stricken, sorrowing parents, her daughter Lenchen and son-in-law Prince Christian of Schleswig-Holstein, who live nearby at Cumberland Lodge on the grounds of Windsor Castle. Queen Victoria knows that this meeting is likely to tear afresh at the new wound, for the Christians as well as for herself. But with that sad encounter concluded, the observant and caring Marie Mallet could take comfort from her belief that the Queen had felt less oppressed after seeing Lenchen (Mallet, 1968, p. 215). "The Queen seemed a little better last night, it was the relief of getting the agonizing interview with Princess Christian over...."

However, the next day, 8 November, Victoria must consult with Prince Christian about a troubling, distasteful problem of another of her Schleswig-Holstein grandchildren. Lenchen and Christian's daughter Princess Marie Louise (Louie) had made an unhappy marriage to the gay Prince Aribert of Anhalt, who was now falsely claiming to be the injured party and suing to have the marriage annulled. "Not feeling very well" the Queen concludes on 8 November, likely a considerable understatement. But the Queen, despite her post-mortem idealization of Albert and propensity for maudlin

57

sentimentality, often gave solidly practical marital advice to granddaughters and members of her household. Doubtlessly based on her own experience, she is recalled as having said that the problems of life *begin* with marriage. In the Anhalt case, whatever the outcome of the marriage was to be (Princess Marie Louise was to remain, if only in name, married for life), the Queen gave unquestioning support and sensibly ordered her granddaughter to return home to England without delay.

p 82 7 November *"Arrived at Windsor about 9.... Felt very tired and out of sorts, so I rested & kept quiet. At 12 dear Lenchen came to see me. It was a sad meeting. She was wonderfully calm & resigned & talked a good deal about those who had been kind to her & had written to her...."*

p 83–84 8 November *"...Saw poor Christian at 6.... I spoke of Louie & her painful affairs, which are settled now. The conduct of Aribert is beyond words disgraceful. Wrote & signed. A Ladies dinner. Not feeling very well.–"*

Over the next three days, the Queen struggles to rally at Windsor and leave behind the gloom and dank mists of Balmoral, a place now and forever to be associated with Christle's death. On 10 November, she makes a strenuous effort to concentrate on the many Cabinet changes proposed by Lord Salisbury.* She also tries to put forward a favorable view of her own functioning, as if trying to convince herself: "Had an excellent night...." But the truth is that her now-complete loss of appetite has not improved at all (it is described as "a disgust for all food"), and most of the time she continues to feel "rather wretched."

---

* Lord Salisbury (Robert Gasgoyne-Cecil, 3rd Marquess of Salisbury) was still at the time Prime Minister and would remain in that office until 11 July 1902.

By the 11th, the Queen is compelled to admit that her condition has deteriorated unspeakably. She has just suffered through a "shocking night," unrestful and filled with pain from her arthritic knees and back. "Draughts" were unavailing. Although she does not blame her lack of relief on the "kind & attentive…and very clever Dr. Bankart," she is looking forward to the return the next day of her usual and much-trusted Ordinary, Sir James Reid.*

---

* Sir James Reid, Bt. (1849–1923) was born in Ellon, Aberdeenshire, the son of a country doctor and veterinarian. He was educated locally, had briefly practiced privately in London and then pursued German language and post-graduate medical studies in Vienna before being recommended for a post with Queen Victoria in 1881. The Queen had been seeking a physician native to Scotland who would also be sufficiently fluent in German to treat visiting family members. The candidate pool of well-regarded, Scottish-born, German-fluent physicians must necessarily have been limited, but Reid fit the bill perfectly, and his blend of candor and humor quickly earned Her Majesty's trust. He was eventually promoted to the ranking position of Physician-in-Ordinary to the Queen, succeeding Sir William Jenner in 1889. Queen Victoria had complete confidence in his skill and judgment, and unlike previous "Ordinaries," who mostly functioned as consultants, Sir James remained with the Queen as her senior physician in residence until her death, accompanying her abroad and to her principal homes at Osborne, Windsor, and Balmoral.

According to Michaela, the 3rd Lady Reid and wife of Sir James's grandson, the Queen "would open her heart to him [Sir James] in conversations varying from whether dogs had souls and an after-life to her hatred of Gladstone and her son Affie's drunkenness. When she was approached with various queries, her reply as often as not was 'Ask Sir James'" (Reid, 2001). (This was also the title of Michaela Reid's full-length biography of Sir James Reid).

That we do not know more of the non-medical concerns that the Queen confided to her physician owes much to Sir James's characteristic discretion. However, one might imagine the Queen asking Sir James if he thought that the late Prime Minister William Gladstone, ever her nemesis in both style and substance, had been consigned to the fires of hell; and, if so, how the tactful but droll Sir James might have answered.

Reid eventually came to be entrusted with the most politically sensitive of Royal family matters. For example, in 1905, four years after Queen Victoria's death, Sir James was assigned the delicate and daunting task of obtaining from the son of a Balmoral factor over 300 "most compromising" letters about John Brown that the Queen had uninhibitedly and unwisely written to the factor; these were letters with which King Edward VII was being blackmailed at the time. Reid was ultimately successful in this endeavor.

Traveling to Osborne on 3 August 1898 to receive his own baronetcy from the Queen, the renowned neurologist William Gowers, a colleague as well as a contemporary of Reid, wrote: "Knowing Sir James Reid well, made the visit especially full of interest. He has a baronetcy—well deserved, indeed, considering how the Queen went thro' the Jubilee affair [the Diamond Jubilee celebrating the Queen's 60 years on the throne in 1897] & his tremendous responsibility. She takes advice from no one else. He is splendidly straightforward

Meanwhile, Marie Mallet's husband Bernard has joined her for a few days at Windsor. On 11 November he writes in his diary (Mallet, 1968 p. 219):

> I had not realised that Prince Christian Victor's death had been such a shock to the Queen. That and all the strain of the last year has told terribly on her, and all about her are really anxious for the first time. Marie says the change in her state since August is alarming; loss of weight, size, appetite &c [sic]. One fears it must be the beginning of the end. But she is strong and has no disease and may probably be nursed back into comparative strength again. One prays indeed that it may be so. Not a hint of all this appears to have reached the outside world.

p 85 9 November "...*I had felt better through the day and free from pain, but I still have a disgust for all food.–*"

p 85–86 10 November "*A very fine day.—Had an excellent night, but my appetite is still very bad.... I saw Ld Salisbury. The principal topic of conversation was of course the changes in the Gov't, which almost amount to a new Cabinet.... A Ladies' dinner. Again feeling rather wretched.–*"

p 87–88 11 November "*Had a shocking night & no draughts could make me sleep as pain kept me awake. Felt very tired & unwell when I got up & was not*

---

honest good Scotchman & has a very close personal position outside professional relations. But he never initiates or suggests. No matter how much he deserves a thing, he always wants to be <u>asked</u>, wisely. This profession owes more to him than will ever be known" (Scott, Eadie, & Lees, 2012, p. 232). Gowers's remark was prescient, as Sir James's most important contribution was yet to come, namely, that of presiding with competence and sensitivity over Queen Victoria's last days and the period immediately following her death. Yet for all his admirable qualities, Reid had at least one minor failing: He was singularly unphotogenic, emerging only as a pale, indistinctly whiskered presence in many group portraits.

able to go to church, to my great disappointment.–…Could do nothing the whole morning. Rested & slept a little.–…Lenchen & Thora came to tea, also Arthur.— Did some signing later & managed to write a letter, but I could not go to dinner & had something to eat in the Audience Room with Beatrice. Arthur came & sat with us afterward. I saw no one else & hoped to have a good night but I felt very restless and uncomfortable. Sir J. Reid returned yesterday. Saw him several times, as well as Dr Bankart who leaves tomorrow. The latter has been most kind & attentive & is very clever.–"

The next few Journal entries reflect the Queen's worry about her insomnia, anorexia and general malaise ("still not feeling equal"). Marie Mallet, in a letter written on 12 November, describes the just-returned Sir James Reid as "anxious" about the Queen's state of health (Mallet, 1968). The renewed fighting in the Ashanti is also a cause for concern; but the Queen somehow fortifies her remaining energy in order to preside over a state Council on the 12th.

At that Council meeting, the Queen masterfully oversees the elaborate protocol involving the exchange of seals required by changes in the Cabinet, she being the only person present with first-hand knowledge of the relevant format and offering evidence that, at this particular moment, her memory for details appears to be intact. Notable also is her ability to empathize with those Cabinet members who have lost power or position in the shuffling of roles. For example, in her Journal entry for the 12th, she writes of one minister: "I said some kind things to him, expressing my regret, but I fear he feels it very much…." However, her alertness and overall cognitive competence have actually been fluctuating, a feature consistent with advancing cerebrovascular disease. The present occasion therefore stands out as an exception to recent norms.

Marie Mallet's letter of 13 November reaches hard for optimism about the Queen's condition, but the hopeful sentiment in one sentence is immediately contradicted by the anxious undertone of the next (Mallet, 1968, p. 217): "The Queen is decidedly better today, slept seven hours and has had naps during the day. She enjoyed her coffee and egg for breakfast but she still has bouts of pain and Sir James is not easy."

There is also a reference in Marie's 13 November letter to the likely *on dit* among members of the Queen's Household, namely, that Her Majesty had no specific disease which could account for her increasingly evident decline. This is the view that had been attributed by Bernard Mallet to his wife, Marie, in his 11 November diary entry. Here is Marie's own comment on the 13th:

> There is no reason why she should not be herself again if she could be made to take more nourishment and I *do* feel more cheerful. Sir James is devoting all his energies to getting her better and I have the utmost confidence in him. He is very nice to me and tells me everything which is a comfort.

This statement represents the impressions of non-medical members of the Royal Household, most of whom were at this point clinging to the hope that the Queen's downhill course was not yet beyond the possibility of reversal; and since Marie Mallet had established a close rapport with Sir James Reid, her descriptions have probably been influenced by his medical perspective as well as the consensus of Household members. The phrase "decidedly better" at the beginning of the letter sounds as if it might have been taken verbatim from Sir James.

Whatever its origin, Marie's belief that the Queen would improve if she could only increase her nutritional intake presumes the absence of a specific condition causing her malaise, insomnia and weight loss. However, the lack of a medical etiology is also a defining requirement for the diagnosis of major depressive disorder. In fact, nowhere in Sir James Reid's or Marie

Mallet's surviving notes and letters is there corroboration for the presence or absence of a physical diagnosis (Reid, 1987), but all persons in close contact with the Queen appear to agree that there is no single medical explanation, other than depression, for Her Majesty's symptoms.

p 88–89 12 November *"Had again not a good night & slept rather late. My lack of appetite worse than ever. It is very trying. The morning was very wet.—Rested & slept a little while. Held a Council in the White Drawing Room shortly after 1. First of all I saw Ld Cross, who gave up the Privy Seal with much regret & said he was very sorry to leave my service. Next came Sir M. White Ridley who gave up the seals of the Home office. I said some kind things to him, expressing my regret, but I fear he feels it very much…. Took a short drive…. Still not feeling equal to dining with the Ladies & had something again with Beatrice last night.–"*

p 89–91 13 November *"Had a better night & was able to take a little breakfast.—A very wet morning, so remained indoors & dozed again for a while.—…Saw M^r. Goschen…he spoke most kindly about dear Christle.—… Feeling decidedly better again.–"*

Queen Victoria's Journal entries have recently oscillated widely, lurching between opposing poles of hope and despair. The Queen might begin, as she does in her entries for both 14 and 15 November, by reporting that she has had some good nights, but these are minor outliers against a prevailing background of nightime insomnia and daytime fatigue. Struggling to remain optimistic, she nevertheless admits on 15 November that she does not feel comfortable "yet"; and Her Majesty's fragility and vulnerability are very apparent to Marie Mallet, who on 14 November wrote (Mallet, 1968, p. 218):

The Queen was decidedly better this morning after a good night but a large luncheon party and shouting to the Princess of Wales [Princess Alexandra, whose deafness was by now nearly complete] exhausted her and she was in pain and very feeble after it.

Marie reprises the hopeful supposition that there is no underlying medical cause of the Queen's anorexia and weakness that cannot be remedied by improved nutrition: "…there is no reason why she should not pick up again and regain her appetite…." However, she also acknowledges that "Sir James has never been so anxious before in all these years" (Mallet, 1968, p. 218).

p 91–92 14 November *"A very fine morning.—Had a good night A Ladies' dinner & afterwards Marie M. read to me in the Drawing room out of the papers, accounts of the fighting there has been in the Ashanti, which is very serious.—"*

p 92 15 November *"Had another very good night.—It rained heavily early, but cleared up later & got quite fine.—Am keeping better, but do not feel comfortable yet.—"*

The 16th of November, although it begins as an unpromising "dark wet day," unexpectedly shows the Queen at her best. She inspects Colonial troops who have come to Windsor and demonstrates that she is still able to summon up her dignity in a way only she can do, a display that stirs others to expressions of loyalty and love. She is not, however, spared from appreciating the ragged condition of her troops, and this sight might very well contribute to the rapid return of her depressed state. But for the moment, depleted though she is, she mobilizes her sense of occasion and her awareness of the mystique of Sovereignty, speaking out with clarity and purpose.

In Marie Mallet's account of that day (Mallet, 1968, p. 220):

...although seeing the Colonial troops was an exertion she got through it well and made them a most touching little speech in a strong voice. Poor men, they all looked wrecks more or less, for they were invalids one and all, but they are fine men and have good honest faces.... Their chaplain introduced them and explained who they were, etc. Poor man, he had his foot bitten off by a mad horse on the veldt [sic] and has lost his leg, I cannot imagine a more horrible accident.

p 93 16 November *"A very dark wet day. After 12 went over to St. George's Hall with Beatrice & the children where I inspected about 100 of the Colonial troops who had been invalided.... Some of the men were very fine looking, all in khaki with felt hats.... An old Australian chaplain, who had lost his leg by the bite of a mad horse, named the different Regiments the men belonged to, as they came by.... I said the following words: 'It is with much pleasure that I welcome you here today, & I thank you warmly for your loyal & devoted service & wish you Godspeed on your way home.' They then gave 3 cheers & a Sergeant called for 'One More Colonial,' which apparently was a particular way of cheering in Australia.—"*

In her entry for 17 November, the Queen continues to mourn Christle. She abominates the conduct of the war by the Boers, who have "instincts of the savage," but is not open to questioning the justice of the British cause. She asserts a vestige of British morality by insisting, as head of state, that there be "no recriminations" against the enemy—whatever that might exactly have meant.

p 94–95 17 November *"Windy & showery & much colder.... Saw Sir Redvers Buller, who returned a week ago. He spoke very kindly & with the greatest regret of dear Christle, whom he had seen looking so well, just before he was taken ill…. He said…he did not in the least expect the war to last for so long, or that there would be such stubborn resistance on the part of the enemy. The Boers were very treacherous and cruel, uniting the instincts of the savage with the most modern appliances for fighting…. When I urged that there should be no recriminations, Sir Redvers said there would be none from him.–"*

By 18 and 19 November, the effects of low appetite and malnutrition are unmistakable, and the wretched nights are increasingly impacting the Queen's days. On 19 November, she notes that she "got up too late" to bid farewell to Arthur and Louischen. Meanwhile: "The sitting through meals, unable to eat anything, is most trying.–"

The late autumn day at Windsor was likely to be "cold, windy & dark," much as noted by the Queen. But since Victoria only rarely views herself as "depressed" in anything like the clinical meaning of the term, or uses that word explicitly, it is easy enough to substitute her report of gloomy weather as a description of her mood state, or at least a mental projection consistent with it. In contrast, the visiting Bernard Mallet did not hesitate to use the word "depressed" when describing Queen Victoria in his own diary entry for 18 November: "Another Sunday at Windsor. The Queen much better but often depressed and nervous" (Mallet, 1968, p. 219). (In what way Bernard found the Queen "much better" is not made clear).

The 19th of November is to be the last day that Marie Mallet, whose waiting period is ending, will see the Queen alive. They take a drive together, but there is nothing in particular to distinguish this final encounter from so many earlier ones over the long and remarkable friendship that dated from 1887: "I drove with the Queen again this afternoon and tried to cheer her a little. I was rather successful and I suppose that is why she takes me so often…." (Mallet, 1968, p. 220).

However, Marie's modesty must not be permitted to leave any ambiguity on this point. Theirs was a relationship of great importance to both. The Queen had frequently sought Marie's company because of her regard for her integrity and gratitude for her devotion. In a way, the maternal aspect of their friendship was reciprocal. For Marie, Queen Victoria had been an obvious motherly figure, and an exceptional one: authoritative, but intuitive and genuinely interested. Her Majesty had spared Marie the critical clarity with which she viewed her own children—before their deaths, anyway. Writing in 1891 to her future husband, Marie described the Queen as:

So anxious I should be thoroughly happy and have no worries, so keen to know all about you and your family...In fact the Queen could not have been kinder or more affectionate than if I had been her own child and this great sympathy is what endears her to all who come within its scope for it is thoroughly genuine. (Mallet, 1968, p. 47).

For the Queen, the much younger Marie had, despite her age, the quality of warmth she had sorely missed in her own mother. Although Queen Victoria tolerated absences among her ladies notoriously poorly, this relationship had been sturdy enough to have survived the temporary breaks caused by Marie's marriage and the birth of her first son.

Queen Victoria's admiration and affection for Marie later extended to her young son Victor. In her letters Marie describes the visit of her nearly two-year-old son to Queen Victoria, his Sovereign, his namesake and also his godmother, in 1895. Having arrived at Buckingham Palace on that occasion, Victor took his mother's hand at the designated moment, and they followed a page down a long corridor to the Queen's apartments. Victor, writes Marie, was happy that day, "gloating over his smart brown velvet blouse and his picturesque pleated muslin collar and ruffles and talking away as if at home.... Victor danced by my side shouting 'Go to Queen, Go to Queen,' to the intense amusement of the maids and pages." Once in the Queen's sitting room he focused immediately on a portrait by Landseer of the Prince Consort's favorite greyhound and murmured "Bootiful dog." The Queen, Marie writes, was "enchanted, no courtier could have spoken better." When he was presented with a small gift, he replied: "Thank-oo kind Queen."The encounter ended with the Queen's suggestion to have him painted, as "he is a beautiful child" (Mallet, 1968, pp. 56–58).

p 95 18 November *"Had a not very good night & my appetite all day was bad.–"*

p 95 19 November *"Had a very fair night, but my appetite much about the same. The day was very cold, windy & dark. Went down to the Mausoleum with Beatrice.—In the afternoon drove with Leila E. [Erroll]* & Marie M.— Lenchen came to tea. Arthur & Louischen left early this morning & I got up too late to see them. They go to Ireland tomorrow.—The sitting through meals, unable to eat anything, is most trying.–"*

From this point on, whenever Queen Victoria encounters anyone who knew or fought alongside Christle, she stops to talk and remember and mourn. On 20 November, it is a Col. Browne, Christle's immediate commander, to whom she speaks. Whether or not, as Browne told her, "all the men of his Batt^n" were, in fact, "in such sorrow," and "loved him so," Victoria certainly was, and did. As has been noted, the origin of Queen Victoria's singular love for this grandson was not well understood, but it began on the day of his birth and must be undoubted. Now, however, Christle's potential

---

* Eliza Amelia, Countess of Erroll, served as a Lady of the Bedchamber to Queen Victoria for various periods between 1873 and 1901.

leadership qualities will never be tested, his future contributions to his Sovereign grandmother and her Empire, moot.

Another factor to consider in appreciating the Queen's state of mind at this point is the responsibility she felt, as head of state, for all wartime losses, including and exemplified by Christle's death. In this aspect she could share in the experiences of her subjects in a way that many in her Government could not; and if her responsibility for the conduct of the war was actually only nominal, the Queen still invested it with the greatest possible seriousness.

p 97 20 November "…*Col:Browne dined…I spoke for some time afterward to Col:Browne about dear Christle, who had served under him in the 60th Rifles & he said he could not express his grief, nor what everyone felt. Notably the officers, but all the men of his Battn were in such sorrow, as they loved him so. They had hoped he would command the Battn one day.—*"

Turning from grief to anxiety, the Queen notes that "darling Vicky's 60th birthday" must now be observed under the worst of all possible circumstances. Implicitly confronting her eldest daughter's desperate condition, she acknowledges on 21 November that she can only "… pray daily that she may suffer less. —" It thus comes as no surprise that the Queen herself has had a "disturbed night" and a "very late" start to her day. On 22 November, even the "charming flowers" she drives with Beatrice to see underscore the passage of time, and she observes wistfully: "So many of the little plants I brought back from abroad have grown into big trees."

On 23 November, the Queen refers obliquely to her ongoing malaise ("not feeling very comfortable") and to her persistent and ever-intensifying loss of appetite, a condition that by now should be described as a frank aversion to food. A trip to the family Mausoleum on the 24th can only intensify the feeling of oppression, even with a diversion to purchase a Shetland pony for her Imperial Russian great-grandchildren.

p 98 21 November *"Darling Vicky's 60ᵗʰ birthday. To think of her, who was so wonderfully active & strong, now so ill & suffering, is heart-breaking… we pray daily that she may suffer less.—Had a disturbed night, which made me very late.–"*

p 99 22 November *"A fine, cold day.—Went with Beatrice to the gardens, & looked at the charming flowers. So many of the little plants I brought back from abroad, have grown into big trees.—After 5 I saw Pᶜᵉ Napoleon & his brother Pᶜᵉ Louis, who came from Farnborough where they had been staying with the Empress. They were both very amiable. Pᶜᵉ Louis is much slighter than his brother & not very like him. He has been serving for some time in the Russian army.— A Ladies' dinner.–"*

p 100 23 November *"Not feeling very comfortable & the dislike for food very great.–"*

p 100 24 November *"A fine morning.—Went down to the Mausoleum with Beatrice & Ena. Looked at some Shetland ponies, for me to give one to Alicky* for her children.…"*

---

* Princess Alix of Hesse and by Rhine, by her marriage to Tsar Nicholas II became the Tsarina Alexandra of All the Russias and was later executed with her husband and five children by the Bolsheviks at Ekaterinberg in 1917. She was a daughter of Queen Victoria's third child and second daughter, Princess Alice, the Grand Duchess of Hesse and by Rhine. Alix and her siblings were raised mostly at Windsor and Osborne by Queen Victoria after their mother's death in the diptheria epidemic in Darmstadt in 1878. Princess Alix was known from childhood as "Alicky."

In the entry for 25 November, the Queen, always curious about the details of death, displays an almost scientific curiosity in Christle's illness, particularly the signs and stages that preceded his demise. There is precedent for this interest. When Prince Albert had been dying, on 14 January 1861, the Queen, upon hearing his gasping, agonal breathing, referred to the experience of witnessing her mother's still-recent death, and said, "This is death—I know it...." (Weintraub, 1988, p. 301).

Nevertheless, it seems rather incongruous for Victoria, that most emotional, even histrionic, of persons, to attempt to achieve objectivity. Yet, for whatever reason, it was clearly important to her to understand exactly what happened to Christle. In the Prince Consort's case, she had been content to lay the blame, quite unfairly, on what she deemed the dissolute behavior of Bertie that had been so disheartening to Albert.

p 102–103 25 November *"A bright morning.—...Before luncheon saw Frank Teck,* who arrived early last night. He told us all about dear Christle's illness & death. There had been no alarm till the 26th, when the respiration became very rapid & the strength gave way. Frank said that there was no doubt it was the malarial fever at the last, which killed him. He seems to have looked after everything in the kindest way, the flowers, the grave, etc. Frank also said Ld Roberts was much worn out, as were many people...."*

When it comes to memorializing those she has loved, no detail is too small for Queen Victoria. Apparently seeking a symbolic prolongation of Christle's foreshortened life, on 26 November, the Queen reports that his horse, which she had ordered shipped from South Africa, and which had "followed" at his funeral, was to live out its days at the Balmoral Dairy Farm. It was felt to be more dignified for Christle's own body to remain forever in South

---

* 'Frank Teck' was Prince Francis of Teck, a brother of Princess May, the Duchess of York.

Africa, near the graves of the men with whom he had fought, unlike that of her son-in-law Liko Battenberg, whose eviscerated corpse had been brought back to England for burial five years earlier preserved in a tub of rum.

The Queen alludes, almost as an afterthought at the end of the 26 November entry, to her continuing "dislike" for food. "Dislike" has by now become a euphemism for a frank aversion to food, and it is seriously worrying, far beyond "tiresome."

The next day, 27 November, the Queen's Journal entry begins with a brief but revealing account of her state of health; this time her malaise is contrasted with the "fine" weather that has continued from the day before. The Queen continues to mourn Christle by taking every possible opportunity to talk about him with soldiers he had known.

p 102 26 November *"A fine day.— Saw dear Christle's 2ⁿᵈ charger, which he had ridden latterly, & which followed at the funeral. It came in the same ship as Frank* [Prince Francis of Teck], *& will remain for the present at the Dairy Farm.—…Feel rather poorly, & the dislike for food still continues, which is very tiresome.…"*

p 103–104 27 November *"Another fine day.—Did not feel very well.… Gen:B* [Brocklehurst, an equerry] *dined. The latter had just returned from S. Africa & looks quite unchanged, never having had a day's ill health. He also praised dear Christle, whom he had seen a great deal of, very much.–"*

On 28 November, the Queen writes about pain. The source of the pain is not specified, but it can be assumed that she is referring to her arthritic knees and perhaps her lower back as well. Like most somatic pain, the Queen's is predictably worse at night in the absence of daytime distractions. What is significant about the pain now experienced by the Queen is its adverse effect on her already insufficient sleep; the Queen is in pain and wakeful most of the night. Sleeping on the sofa well into the following day marks a nearly complete reversal of her sleep cycle: Queen Victoria is now wakeful and restless during the night, and naps or dozes intermittently throughout the day.

Her Majesty concludes the 28 November entry with the admission that she has discussed her health with her Prime Minister, Lord Salisbury. She implies that it was Lord Salisbury himself "who talked a good deal about my health...." However, according to the protocol for audiences with the Sovereign, any discourse on this subject could not have been initiated, and certainly could not have been sustained, without the Queen's tacit approval. What is remarkable is that it occurred at all. The Queen had generally been reticent about her health, especially with political figures, even trusted ones such as this Prime Minister. Lord Salisbury apparently also advised the Queen to go abroad in the coming spring, as she had usually done. This did not happen.

p 104 28 November *"Had a very restless night, with a good deal of pain. Got up very late & when I did felt so tired I could do nothing & slept on the sofa. It was a very wet day & I did not go out at all.... Saw Ld Salisbury after tea, who talked a good deal about my health, the necessity for my going abroad & getting a thorough change to rest.–"*

The next day, 29 November, the Queen reports having had a "good night" and feeling "rather better." This improvement does not simply represent the variations she has recently been reporting from day to day, or even within single days—traversing a narrow range from "terrible" to "rather better" and back again—but instead reflects the temporary emotional lift she has often experienced when meeting with troops.

On this day Queen Victoria inspects the same contingent of Life Guards to whom she had bid farewell a year before. She proudly includes in her

Journal entry the text of her address to the troops, a message that after Christle's death is heartfelt, and one that she believes to especially stirring. The connection with Christle is made explicit when she honors his subaltern. This entry, and the next, describing her review of Canadian troops on 30 November, together show Queen Victoria at her charismatic best, raising not only the spirits of the soldiers, but momentarily also her own.

p 105–107 29 November *"Had a good night & felt rather better.* [Inspected the Life Guards] ... *& addressed the troops: 'It is with feeling of great pleasure & deep thankfulness, that I welcome you home after your gallant & arduous services in the war in South Africa, just a year after I bid you farewell! Alas! the joy at your safe return is clouded over by the memory of sad losses of many a valuable life, which I in common with you all have to deplore.' The men gave 3 cheers & marched off to the Barracks.... Afterwards Lenchen brought in Lieut:Blundell of the 60th Rifles who was Christle's greatest friend & his subaltern. He had not been with him when he died, but was sent for at once & saw him afterwards, looking so peaceful, as if only asleep. He said Christle had been so well the whole time, & spoke very nicely of him, & of how much he had been admired & respected. I gave Lieut:Blundell the 4th class of the Victorian order, as a remembrance of his great friendship & devotion...."*

p 108 30 November *"A very fine bright morning, which was very satisfactory for the visit of the Canadian troops.—I had a very fair night, but my appetite still bad.—At 12 went in the carriage with Beatrice & Alice* & inspected the Canadian troops, to the number of 240, in the Quadrangle. They were*

---

* Princess Alice of Albany was a daughter of the Queen's eighth child and fourth son, Prince Leopold, Duke of Albany. Princess Alice, who married a brother of Princess May, Prince Alexander of Teck, died in 1981, the last surviving grandchild of Queen Victoria. Her brother was the ill-starred Prince Charles Edward, Duke of Albany and Duke of Saxe-Coburg and Gotha.

drawn up just as all previous occasions, receiving me with a Royal Salute & the Colonel, Col:Otter, was presented to me, after which they marched past & drew up close to the carriage, when I addressed the following words to them. 'I am very glad to see you here today & I express my warm thanks for the admirable services rendered in the war by the Canadian troops. I wish you all a safe & happy return to your homes....' They all said their men & Canada would never forget their day at Windsor.–"

The date of 1 December marks the first day of the last full month of the Queen's life. The pendulum now swings more broadly than before, from "an excellent night" to a "dreadfully dark" day and a feeling of being "rather unwell the whole evening"; but on balance, the trend is firmly in the direction of "unwell." This date is also the 56th birthday of the Princess of Wales, for whom the Queen has in the past had ambivalent feelings: disdain for the phlegmatic, undisciplined aspects of her personality and her lax approach to raising children, co-existing with admiration for her charm, modesty, and exceptional beauty.

p 109 1 December *"Had an excellent night.—Dear Alix's* birthday, God bless her!—It was a horrid dark wet day. Did not go out in the morning.—Lenchen & Abby came to luncheon.—Drove with Alice & Cecilia D. It was dry but dreadfully dark, & one could see nothing. Felt rather unwell the whole evening.–"*

By 2 December, judging from her entry for that date, the Queen is thoroughly miserable. She continues to lie awake for most of the night, feeling exhausted during the day. Her feeble appetite has flickered out entirely. Her mourning for Christle will never cease nor ease, and she

---

* The Queen is referring here to the Princess of Wales, later Queen Alexandra, the wife of her eldest son. The other Alix in the family, Queen Victoria's granddaughter Princess Alix of Hesse, by marriage the Tsarina of All the Russias, was more frequently known as "Alicky."

continues to make special mention of every encounter with his comrades or servants. The glorious Victorian age seems destined to end in its Sovereign namesake's anxiety over the war in South Africa and sadness at its long casualty lists.

p 110 2 December *"After a very wretched night, I passed a very miserable day & could neither go out nor leave my room. Missed being able to go to church & hearing a very fine sermon from Dean Farrar, which annoyed me very much.— Slept a good deal, & as my repulsion for food was very great, went to neither luncheon or dinner. Beatrice read & played a little to me.—Forgot to say that I saw yesterday dear Christle's soldier servant, a very good man, who had been with him 6 years, & all through this dreadful war. There has been some severe fighting under Gen:Paget. Ld Roberts has given up the supreme command to Ld Kitchener.—* In the evening Beatrice read me some Prayers, etc.–"*

On 3 December the Queen reports that she had "a better night," a doubtful assertion that has by now been attempted many times, but she starts this day slowly, as is now usual for her, feeling sleepy throughout the morning. Later she manages to go through the motions of Sovereignty, these being mostly ceremonial to begin with, but she displays her genuine interest in people and a generous capacity to admire characteristics not her own. For example, she finds the Maharanee of Barada to be "still pretty"; and young Lord Ampthill[†] and his wife are described as "both very tall & she, very pretty." Queen Victoria herself was never more than five feet in height and

---

* Herbert Horatio Kitchener, Lord Kitchener of Khartoum, later 1st Earl Kitchener, was a noted military leader and strategist in Victorian-era imperial campaigns.

† This Lord Ampthill was Oliver Villiers Russell, 2nd Baron Ampthill, son of the first Lord Ampthill. The younger Lord Ampthill had been an athlete—a rower at Eton and Oxford. At this time he was Governor of Madras, later becoming the acting Viceroy of India.

only briefly attractive in her youth, before the combined effects of a strong appetite and nine pregnancies began to show.

p 111 3 December *"A very dull dreary day.—Had a better night..—Went out with Alice.—Was very sleepy & slept a little before luncheon. Before tea I received the Maharanee of Barada, whom I had met several times before. She is still pretty and speaks now quite fluent English. After tea I received Ld Ampthill who is going as Governor to Madras & knighted him handing him the Star of India, after he had kissed hands, but he can only wear it after getting to his destination. I then saw L^y Ampthill. They are both very tall & she, very pretty.* [List of names] *dined. I was able to dine, but could scarcely eat anything.–"*

The following day, 4 December, is again dark and wintry. After a conversation with her cousin Prince George, the Duke of Cambridge, Queen Victoria is disappointed that her son Arthur is not to succeed George Cambridge as Commander in Chief of the Army, but the Queen is too much of a realist to have believed otherwise. The low light and George's view that the war in South Africa has not been "going quite well" serve only to heighten the prevailing doldrums.

p 112 4 December *"...In the afternoon drove with Helen really quite in the dark.... After tea saw George C* who talked a great deal about the army & his great wish that Arthur should become Adjutant Gen., which I was rather in doubt about. George also said he did not think things were going quite well in S. Africa.–"*

---

* Prince George, 2nd Duke of Cambridge, was the Queen's first cousin and also the maternal uncle of Princess May, the Duchess of York.

The Queen now tries to rouse herself from torpor and sadness. When she becomes "weary" indoors on 5 December, she drives out, always her preferred way to relax and restore and think clearly, this time even in the dark wintry rain. The bravery and unselfishness of Princess Thora, Lenchen's daughter, are honored by Queen Victoria in the 5 December entry, a reference to this modest granddaughter's willingness to attend to the Queen's needs despite her own grief over the death of her brother, Christle. The devoted and self-effacing Thora is more than worthy of such recognition, and the two grief-stricken women take the drive together. For the Queen, music is another consolation which reliably "soothes" (6 December).

p 113 5 December *"A very dark & completely rainy day.—I had a very fair night, but otherwise no better.—I got so weary indoors, that I thought I would take ½ an hour's drive with Thora, who is wonderfully brave & unselfish.–... Felt very uncomfortable after dinner.—Much grieved to hear that poor Baroness Schroeder, who had been very ill since last week, & had been taken to London, had died this afternoon. She will be a great loss to poor Lenchen, whose near neighbour & friend she was.–"*

p 114 6 December *"...Gerry Liddell* came & played after dinner, as music soothes me. Only the Ladies dined.–"*

On 7 December the Queen gives way fully to despair, categorically stating that "nothing did any good" to induce sleep and that the weather was "dark and gloomy." The image of somber organ music being played for a winter afternoon recital in the chapel only accentuates the bleakness of the setting. By evening the Queen is too tired to attempt to do anything, yet

---

* The Hon. Georgiana Liddell was a former Maid of Honor to Queen Victoria and subsequently a close friend.

she is unable to sleep—paradoxically, too tired to sleep. "Remained in my room, resting on the sofa," is a memorable snapshot, a succinct image of the paralysis of depression.

p 114–115 7 December *"I had a very bad night, nothing did any good, & got only about 1 hour's sleep. I did not get up till late, & had a little breakfast alone in my room.—Went out for ½ an hour with Thora & then rested & slept soundly, but did not go to luncheon.—Drove with Thora and Alice. It was very dark and gloomy.—After tea Sir Walter Parratt played on the organ in the Chapel.—I felt very poorly in the evening & could not go to dinner. Remained in my room, resting on the sofa.–"*

Meanwhile, Vicky's illness continues to be very worrying, and in her 8 December entry the Queen makes no further attempt to dilute the horror of her daughter's suffering. The Kaiser, Vicky's erratic, labile son, continues to send conflicting messages: admiration for all things English and for Queen Victoria herself, alternating with a mix of envy, hostility and even paranoia. Then, the sad misadventure of Princess Marie Louise's marriage to Prince Aribert of Anhalt is at last, after prolonged and distasteful negotiations, reaching a legally negotiated annulment.

p 115 8 December *"Had a very good night.—Took a turn with Thora & when I came in I did a little signing.—Heard from Beatrice* [traveling in Germany] *that she had seen dear Vicky, who was so delighted at her coming.... Beatrice said that though she has not altered in face, it was too piteous to see her so helpless & suffering such terrible pain.—...Felt wretched but managed to come to dinner.... I spoke afterwards with Frank* [Lascelles] *who says William* [the Kaiser] *is most anxious to be on terms with us. He also spoke about Louie's affairs, which he hopes will soon be satisfactorily settled.–"*

The next day, 9 December, the Queen reports that she did not feel well early in the day and was "so wretched" by tea-time. Her comment "though they say I am getting better," hints at a justified skepticism.

p 116 9 December *"Had a fair night but got up late.—Was able to go to church.—Did not feel well, though they say I am getting better.—Louise & Lorne* came for luncheon & to stay the night.—She and Victoria Battenberg drove with me.—Felt so wretched, that I had no tea & stayed & rested in my room.... Had a family dinner...."*

"Fair" nights such as reported by the Queen on 10 December are fast becoming the exception, and even then, the rating of "fair" is a generous one, considering the long bouts of insomnia and restlessness we now know that the Queen has been enduring. Queen Victoria is again moved by praise for the sadly unused talents of the late Prince Christle.

p 116–117 10 December *"Had a fair night. A lovely bright morning.—Out for a short while with Thora & in the afternoon drove with Lenchen & Louisa A. [Antrim]. It had become dull & dark.—Had tea with Lenchen, Thora & Alice, & later saw Ld Wolseley,† who spoke most kindly & touchingly of dear Christle saying what a loss he was & how he had looked upon him as one of the rising men in the army. L^d and L^y Wolseley, Ld Abercromby, Sir Condie Stephen, Luise A., Sir A. Bigge & Col:Davidson dined.–"*

---

* John Campbell, known by the courtesy title of Marquess of Lorne, abbreviated to "Lorne" in the family, was the husband of Princess Louise, Queen Victoria's sixth child and fourth daughter. By this time he had recently become the 9th Duke of Argyll but was still called "Lorne" by close relations.

† Garnet Joseph Wolseley, 1st Viscount Wolseley, was a Field Marshall and Commander-in-Chief of British armed forces from 1895 to 1900.

Parsing her words, the Queen writes on 11 December that she has just had a "tolerably good night." This would seem an improvement over "fair" in a scale known only to the Queen herself. But by any measure even this "tolerably good night" has been unrestful and not at all recuperative.

It is difficult to give much credence to the sugar-coated account of Vicky by Beatrice, who has just returned from Germany. This report probably reflected Beatrice's well-intended but baseless attempt to reassure the Queen. Even with intermittent doses of morphine, "cheerful at times" is an unrealistic description of a person whose metastatic disease has invaded and eroded her spine.

Meanwhile, at Osborne, Sir Francis Laking,* the Prince of Wales's doctor, has been substituting for Sir James Reid, who is away. Laking, whose diagnostic acumen and medical skills are privately disparaged by Sir James, urges the Queen in what probably seemed even then to be a futile gesture, to "get over" her "squeamishness" about food. She should simply "get over" her severe anorexia, in effect, will it so. Laking also recommends taking "a little milk and whiskey several times a day" as an appetite stimulant.

But the cumulative effects of insomnia and malnutrition cannot be denied, and the Queen, weakening daily, is now overwhelmingly fatigued. On 11 December she feels too tired to rouse herself before evening to see her grandson, "Georgie," the Duke of York, who is now second, after his father, in the direct line to the throne, the "heir to the heir" and the person on whom her hopes for the future of the monarchy rest.

The Duke of York, his Teck brother-in-law, Prince Alexander, and his Duchess (Princess May), had come to Windsor to see the Queen and have now been waiting all day. They will not depart without a proper leave-taking. That the Queen keeps them waiting anxiously for so long is yet another

---

* Sir Francis Laking, Bt. (1847–1914) was Physician-in-Ordinary and Surgeon-Apothecary to the Prince of Wales and was called upon to "fill in" for James Reid on the infrequent occasions when the latter was away or otherwise unavailable.

indication of how far her condition has deteriorated. Also, regaining some energy late in the day or by early evening should not be read as a sign of improvement, but should be understood as a feature consistent with the diurnal variation of mood frequently experienced by persons suffering from a major depressive disorder.

p 117–118 *11 December "Had a tolerably good night.—Beatrice returned* [from Germany] *after 10, having had a good crossing. She described dear Vicky as not being much altered in face & being even cheerful at times, but terribly ailing & suffering. Her only occupation is reading, & being read to, as she cannot use her hands.—Went down to the Mausoleum with Lenchen, Beatrice, & Louie, & placed some wreaths there.–...Saw Sir Francis Laking for some time after tea. He encouraged me by saying he thought I should in time get over this unpleasant dislike for food & squeamishness as well as the great discomfort I suffer from & he recommended my taking a little milk & whiskey several times a day—Georgie & May arrived bringing Alge Teck* with them, but I did not see them before dinner, as I was feeling so tired.–"*

By now it is almost certain that word of the Queen's infirmity had been seeping out of the Court and the Royal Household, themselves whispering galleries of rumors, into Society and beyond to the wider public. As a consequence, an event was hastily arranged for the sake of appearances and to avert widespread anxiety. The Queen's 12 December entry describes this outing.

p 118 12 December *"Had a good night.... At ½ p 12 I drove with Beatrice & May to the Town Hall, where a sale of Irish Industries was arranged, which I*

---

* "Alge" Teck was Prince Alexander George of Teck, the youngest brother of Princess May, the Duchess of York.

looked at before it was offered, being rolled around to each stall & the different ladies at each, being presented to me. Some of them I knew quite well.... There were some very pretty things & I made various purchases.–"

The 13th of December finds the Queen still clinging to the duties of the Sovereign, although with great effort. She convenes a Council, talks with an injured soldier who had been brought to meet her by Princess Louise, and formally receives the new Brazilian minister. However, it is becoming clear that Queen Victoria cannot maintain this level of activity very much longer. She is now almost completely unable to eat.

p 119–120 13 December *"...Had another good night.—A very wet morning.— Drove down to the Mausoleum with Alice in a closed carriage.—Held a Council before luncheon. In the afternoon drove with Alice & Louise, the latter having just arrived & she presented to me at the door, a New Zealand officer, a Col:Francis, who had been invalided from S. Africa.... At 5 received the new Brazilian minister.... Rested a good long time after tea.... My appetite as bad as ever, can hardly eat anything.–"*

Then, 14 December—frequently cited by the Queen as the "dreadful 14th," the anniversary of Albert's death—comes around again. For 39 years the memorial service held on this date at the family Mausoleum at Frogmore on the grounds of Windsor Castle has been the pre-eminent event of her annual late-autumn stay at Windsor, if not her sole purpose in being there at that time, and the most important observance of her entire calendar (Albert's birthday being a close second).

This year the anniversary evokes as much emotion as ever in the vulnerable, failing Queen. She writes that the sad service was enhanced by a "very beautiful" special prayer and "lovely" music. Yet in the past this observance had not always been so oppressively weepy; she at other times was able to view her marriage to Albert, and marriage generally, in more pragmatic terms. But for now the weather and the atmosphere remain "dull & dark," and the wrenching leave-taking by Georgie and May, when it at last took place at the Mausoleum itself, could only have contributed to the melancholy tone of the occasion. By day's end the Queen is feeling "unwell again," a description ambiguous enough to suggest both depression and physical malaise.

p 120–121 14 December *"This sad day so full of terrible memories returned again…. Drove down for the service at the Mausoleum…all the family attending it…. The special prayer was very beautiful & the music lovely. May & Georgie took leave of me at the Mausoleum. In the afternoon, which was dull & dark, drove with Alix.—Feeling very unwell again & it was a great effort to go to dinner… ."*

On 15 December the Queen records that, despite a "very late" start, by the early evening she had summoned the energy to personally award five Victoria crosses and an Albert Medal to a select group of deserving officers and men. This tribute appears to have been a deeply felt ceremony conducted by a visibly frail Sovereign. Then, on the next day, 16 December, the inexorable process of implosion speeds up again. Now she can barely function at all, sleeping most of the day after a "very bad" night and, in a rare and therefore significant move, she cuts short her audience with Lord Salisbury.

On the 17th, her last day at Windsor before crossing the Solent to Osborne for Christmas, the Queen lays a wreath on her mother's grave in the Mausoleum at Frogmore, a last act of reconciliation in what had been a fraught and fractious relationship, perhaps offered at this juncture in recognition of her own impending death. Dozing, and dazed, she seems barely fit enough for the short journey to Osborne she is to undertake the following day. After that there will be no travel of any kind.

**HRH The Prince Alfred, Duke of Edinburgh
and Duke of Coburg ("Affie")**

**HM Queen Victoria with her daughter,
HRH The Princess Beatrice (Princess Henry of Battenberg)**

**HSH Princess Victoria Mary of Teck ("May"),
later Queen Consort to HM King George V**

HSH Prince Henry of Battenberg ("Liko")

**HSH Prince Christian Victor of
Schleswig-Holstein ("Christle")**

Sir James Reid, Bt., Physician-in-Ordinary to Queen Victoria

**HSH Princess Helena Victoria
of Schleswig-Holstein ("Thora")**

**HRH Albert Edward, The Prince of Wales ("Bertie"),
later HM King Edward VII**

**HRH Alexandra, The Princess of Wales ("Alix"),
later Queen Consort to HM King Edward VII**

p 121 15 December *"...Got out very late with Beatrice & Alice. At 5 gave five Victoria Crosses ...to officers & men who had much distinguished themselves in S. Africa, also an Albert Medal to a naval officer.–"*

p 122 16 December *"Had a very bad night & only got up late, having my breakfast alone.... Was very tired & drowsy after luncheon, so rested & slept most of the afternoon.—Lenchen came to tea, after which I saw Ld Salisbury, but I did not feel up to a very lengthened conversation.—Was unable to go to dinner. Beatrice sat with me afterwards & read a little to me.–"*

p 122 17 December *"Another bad night. Got out very late & drove with Beatrice to the Mausoleum going over to Mama's* in the pony chair and placing wreaths there.... Lenchen came to tea again. I rested afterwards & dozed...."*

---

* Queen Victoria's mother was born Princess Marie Louise Victoire of Saxe-Coburg Saalfeld. She later became a widow, the Dowager Princess of Leiningen, and then, by marriage to the Queen's father Prince Edward, Duchess of Kent. Fearful of the malicious intentions of her English brothers-in-law, of whom the youngest three had been displaced in the order of succession by the birth of Princess Victoria of Kent, and unfamiliar with the language and customs of her adopted country, the again-widowed Duchess was poorly advised. Not only did she refuse the young Princess any meaningful measures of personal freedom or privacy, but also, until the Queen's succession, she insisted that Victoria share her bedroom. Inflaming the situation further, the Duchess repeatedly offended the reigning King, William IV; and she failed to intervene when her Comptroller and likely lover, Sir John Conroy, bullied the princess in a crude attempt to gain advantage.

Victoria's succession to the throne at the age of eighteen and subsequent marriage to her cousin Prince Albert were therefore experienced by the new Queen Regnant as events that liberated her from an oppressive regime. One of her first acts after succeeding to the throne was to banish Sir John Conroy from Court. As Queen, Her Majesty's relationship with her mother remained distant until a partial reconciliation was achieved near the end of the Duchess's life. The Duchess of Kent had been entombed with others of the Queen's family in the Mausoleum at Frogmore, on the grounds of Windsor Castle.

References

Mallet, V. (Ed.). (1968). *Life with Queen Victoria: Marie Mallet's letters from court, 1887–1901.* Houghton Mifflin Company: Boston, MA, pp. 56–58, 215, 217, 218, 219, 220.

Reid, M. (2001). Sir James Reid, B^t: Royal apothecary. *Journal of the Royal Society of Medicine, 94*(4):194–195.

Scott, A., Eadie, M., & Lees, A. (2012). *William Richard Gowers 1845–1915: Exploring the Victorian brain.* Oxford University Press: Oxford, UK, p. 232.

Victoria, R.I. (1900). *Queen Victoria's Journal (Royal Archives), 7 November–17 December, 1900,* pp. 82–122.

Weintraub, S. (1988). *Victoria: An intimate biography.* Truman Talley Books/ E.P. Dutton: New York, NY, p. 301.

5. Osborne House from 18 December, 1900 until the Queen's Death on 22 January, 1901: "*Staring* [sic] *night.*"

On 18 December, the Queen arrives at Osborne by mid-afternoon nearly prostrate with fatigue. Lady Churchill, a confidante and Lady-in-Waiting, is shocked by the deterioration she sees as Victoria disembarks on the Isle of Wight; and she remarks to the person standing next to her that Her Majesty seems a "dying woman." The Queen's own entry for the day does nothing to contradict Lady Churchill's dire prediction. She writes vaguely about having "some dinner …in the room in which we generally breakfast" and closes by noting some more "very unsatisfactory" news from South Africa.

Sir James Reid, who accompanied Queen Victoria from Windsor to Osborne, comments on this journey, the last the Queen would make alive, in a letter (Reid, 1987, p. 198). "Her Majesty stood the journey well, but was very tired, and had a long fit of nerve restlessness and depression after our arrival till she went to sleep. Was with her very often." The "nerve restlessness and depression" cited by Reid suggest what is commonly referred to by psychiatrists as "agitated depression."

p 123 18 December *"Had a very bad night & scarcely slept at all.—Breakfasted late & left for Osborne at 11.40, with Beatrice & Ena, Thora meeting us at the station. Drino had arrived early from Wellington College.—Slept for an hour in the train, & then I had a little broth, but I could not take much. Embarked on the "Alberta" at 2. It was rather rough just outside Portsmouth, but became quite calm afterwards. Arrived up at the house about 3.30. Felt too tired to do anything & dozed for short while.—Had some dinner with Beatrice & Thora, in the room in which we generally breakfast.—There were very unsatisfactory news from S. Africa, the Boers being terribly active all over the country.–"*

On the night of the 18th the Queen suffers from her usual early insomnia, that is, difficulty initiating sleep, a troubling condition that Beatrice's spiritless reading-aloud not only fails to relieve but seems paradoxically to exacerbate. The Queen writes that Beatrice's effort "… quite failed in its object, as it only made me wakeful.—"Then, when she finally achieves a light state of sleep, it is followed by long periods of wakefulness. Queen Victoria's night then concludes with a feeling of exhaustion lasting the entire morning.

The Queen's first full day at her beloved Osborne, 19 December, conforms to the problematic pattern that has by now become firmly established. The day begins slowly and late; nothing is accomplished. From now on, all her meals, meagre as they are, will be taken in her own room and no longer in the dining room with her Ladies or other members of the Household (Reid, 1987).

On the 19th the Queen does not report feeling any better by the early evening, as she has done on several of the days immediately prior. She goes back to bed at 10, "feeling quite tired out" after a day filled with very little. There is here a new level of emotional flatness, of joylessness, with no mention at all of any pleasure in returning to her island retreat, this place of refuge and reminiscence which has always before been a dependable source of consolation.

p 123–124 19 December *"Had another very bad night. An attempt was made to induce me to sleep by Beatrice reading aloud but it quite failed in its object, as it*

only made me wakeful.—Had a very late breakfast & did not go out.... Rested &
slept a little.... In the afternoon drove with Thora, but could not go to any meals
& did not do anything all day.–...I went to bed at 10, feeling quite tired out.– "

On 20 December there is more evidence, if any is needed, to make the case
that the Queen's nighttime sleep pattern is disrupted beyond all remedy.
She sleeps all morning and cannot begin her day until the afternoon. She
continues to eat virtually nothing save for "a little soup," and she remains
"uncomfortable"; the term "uncomfortable" is recognizable from previous
entries as Queen Victoria's euphemism for unrelenting pain, but it now also
includes unwelcome new elements of agitation and restlessness. However,
the previous "uncomfortable" has now advanced to "very uncomfortable &
miserable," denoting a higher degree of severity in the Queen's normally
bland lexicon. After resting, she dictates a Journal entry to Thora and then
manages to do a small amount of work, signing a few documents that require
the Sovereign's official approval; but her usual remedy, driving out, is denied
her as it rains all day.

The 21st of December passes in much the same way, with the Queen's
sleep pattern and food intake unchanged from the previous day, although
the weather has now improved a little, allowing her to drive with Princess
Thora to the Isle of Wight's shore, for her a place of happiness and
inspiration.

p 124 20 December *"Had a little sleep the first part of the night, but then was*
awake for several hours, & when I did go to sleep again, did not awake till the
middle of the day. Had no appetite & did not go out, as it poured all day. Beatrice
played a little on the piano to me in the afternoon. I felt very uncomfortable &
miserable. Rested & then dictated to Thora, & signed a little afterwards.—Had a
little soup in dear Albert's room & Thora came & sat with me, afterwards Beatrice
also came, & I went to bed after 10.–"

p 125 21 December *"Had a much better night, but slept again until nearly 1.—Had a little soup & then drove with Thora round by the sea.—Rested when I came home & had a little tea. Later I dictated to Thora & then signed.—Had a little soup in my room & went early to bed.–"*

For all of the Queen's references to being improved or better, as in the 22 December entry below, and the corroborating observations made by those around her, in truth Her Majesty's condition is worsening daily. In this day's entry the counter to "rather better" is her poor vision, which is now, for all practical purposes, nil. With dwindling energy, she manages to receive the children and grandchildren who have come to Osborne for Christmas, greeting them separately, but only for a "moment" each. Between the lines, such as the one that mentions a breakfast she "really liked," and despite the euphemisms she typically offers, the direction of her strength and functioning is sharply downward.

On the 22nd the Queen sadly acknowledges the devotion of her servants—"all my good people"—this flush of emotion in apparent anticipation of a final parting from them. Her warmth toward servants has long co-existed with the cool correctness she has displayed with persons more privileged and especially with those whose politics she despises. She has always derived solace from emotional intimacy with servants, not confined to her complicated, erotically-tinged relationships with John Brown and the Munshi.

The capacity to elicit devotion from the people who served her was an important component of Queen Victoria's magnetism and mystique. In the past, she had made a point of insisting that her children and grandchildren should not display a formal or distant attitude toward servants, particularly as she had herself often shared greater warmth and affection with them than with her own family. As has been shown, she had been thoroughly irked by the contemptuous attitude of her son Affie toward John Brown and her other servant-confidants.

p 125 22 December *"I slept a little at first & then was rather disturbed, after which I slept on again till ¼ to 12, at which I was very annoyed. I got up & had some breakfast, which I really liked, then drove out with Thora. I am rather better, but still see very badly.—All my good people, my maids & Indian servants are indefatigable, & so anxious to do anything they can for me.—Lenchen, & Arthur & Louischen, who have come to spend Xmas* [sic] *here with their children, arrived, & I saw them each separately for a moment.-"*

As Christmas nears, it can be readily appreciated from the 23 December entry that Queen Victoria's world is contracting. The day passes uneventfully; Beatrice tries to soothe or distract her by playing the piano; and the Queen retires after her "little supper."

One can imagine that the loss of her productivity must have been painful to the Queen, who despite her reluctance to appear in public after the death of Albert, was nothing if not serious about her work and her role; but here she accepts only that sleeping until noon has "annoyed" her.

Because the Queen can do so little, and there are suggestions of loss of alertness, the possibility of underlying cognitive impairment now emerges. Despite these suspicions, nothing definitive can be concluded as of 23 December 1900. The Queen's ability to recall the exact protocol for the transfer of seals at the 12 November Council meeting had been reassuring, but transient periods of improved cognitive functioning can also be consistent with an overall trajectory of decline.

The most valuable source on the Queen's cognitive state, Sir James Reid's working medical notes, were mostly destroyed. These notes and other sensitive documents written or used by Reid were burned after his death by his son at his request; and the accounts of the Queen's last months of life in *Ask Sir James*, are therefore, as their author Lady (Michaela) Reid acknowledges, based largely on letters and on Reid's surviving "scrapbooks" (Reid, 1987).

Before the Queen's presumed cerebrovascular events during her final days and hours, the only explicit reference in *Ask Sir James* to cognitive deficits comes in July 1900, soon after the Queen arrives to spend the summer at Osborne, and it is loosely attributed to a letter Reid had received from Sir Francis Laking. Based on the Laking letter, Michaela Reid summarizes Queen Victoria's functioning during the summer of 1900 as follows (Reid, 1987, p. 195): "Her memory, which formerly had always served her well, was letting her down, and she was forced to exert additional mental effort which tired her." (To an old-age physician, this description conforms more closely to the clinical entity of mild cognitive impairment than to dementia *per se*.)

Five months later, in his confidential letter on 2 December to the Prince of Wales, Reid reported that neither he nor the consulting Dr. Barlow (Physician Extraordinary*) had observed any evidence of "organic disease." This last comment appears to have been intentionally obscure and should be interpreted as Reid's attempt to present a hopeful picture for the Prince of Wales (Reid, 1987, p. 197).

p 126 23 December *"A fine morning. I had a fairly good night, but again slept till nearly 12, which annoyed me very much.—My appetite very indifferent.—… Had some broth, & later Beatrice played to me on the piano. I rested again & then dictated to Thora & signed. I felt rather exhausted.—After my little supper, Beatrice & Arthur came up to me for a short while.–"*

---

* The position of "Physician Extraordinary" (literally "Extra-Ordinary") ranked below that of Sir James Reid's senior role as "Physician-in-Ordinary."

On Christmas Eve, the Queen's thickening cataracts prevent her from enjoying the festive sight of the tree and lights and gifts, all laid out beautifully in the Durbar Room of Osborne House. She acknowledges feeling "melancholy," but attributes this state solely to her poor vision, whereas by this time, more realistically, it is a broad general description of her emotional and physical condition. The frequently contradictory Queen Victoria, self-indulgent in many ways, was also a very disciplined person with a deep admiration for military culture and decorum. Most likely she is now reluctant to acknowledge depression without attributing it to readily identifiable external causes, lest it suggest a weakness of character.

The Prince of Wales had anticipated that the Christmas festivities would "occupy her mind and take her…out of herself" (Reid, 1987, p. 199). Princess Beatrice, who unlike her brother lived with the Queen and saw the situation at firsthand, held out no such hopes that the holiday celebrations would revive her mother. In a letter to Vicky, the Empress Frederick, Beatrice wrote: "She was very depressed, and generally weak, her sight is so very bad and she could hardly see all her pretty presents." Her spirits still low, the Queen seems to derive at most some pallid pleasure from the exchange of gifts with family and Household members, following tradition in what she may realize are to be her last weeks of life. One of her gifts from Lenchen, thoughtful but definitely not cheering, was a miniature of the late lamented Christle, in enamel and set with sapphires (Reid, 1987).

p 126–127 24 December *"I got up a little earlier & had in fact slept better, not having laid awake long.—At 6…went to the Durbar Room, where the Xmas tree & present tables were arranged. I felt very melancholy as I see so badly.—I received lovely things, amongst which an enamel of dear Christle, set with little sapphires, given by Lenchen…. I gave all my personal servants their usual presents & my children gave those for the Ladies & Gentlemen. Took a little supper in my room & then Beatrice came up & played to me.–"*

Queen Victoria awakens on Christmas morning already feeling hopeless, having spent a restless night during which "every remedy that was tried failed in making me sleep." Not only does every remedy fail, but as has been frequently happening, the "remedies" themselves seem to produce precisely the results least desired: "...when I wished to get up I fell asleep again, which was too provoking.—"

On her first drive of the day, at one in the afternoon, the Queen is told by Lenchen that her companion and friend for over 50 years, Jane, Lady Churchill, a Lady of the Bedchamber—the same person who had famously pronounced Queen Victoria "a dying woman" when she observed her weakened condition upon arrival at the Isle of Wight on 18 December—had herself suffered a cardiac event during the night. Somewhat defensively, Her Majesty replies with an "I told you so," to the effect that she had questioned the wisdom of Lady Churchill's decision to come to Osborne again this year, isolated as it was from the metropolis, after she [Lady Churchill] had had a similar illness the last year.

On returning from her drive, the Queen encounters Sir James Reid, who had been awaiting her return to discuss Lady Churchill's condition. Sir James emphasized the seriousness of the situation but held back the fact that Lady Churchill had already died. Apparently he intended to break the news in stages. The Queen, whose first question to Reid has to do with the implications for her own staffing, is advised by him that she "most decidedly" should send for another lady. But she is badly shaken.

To regain her composure, the Queen immediately sets out on another drive, this time with Thora and Prince Arthur's wife, Louischen. During this second outing Her Majesty is able to think more clearly, at which point she acknowledges her love for her friend and concern over her condition. Then, "directly I returned," she sends again for Sir James, who was already on his way, now prepared to bring her the devastating message that Lady Churchill had died: "...all was over." Actually, according to Michaela Reid, Sir James had found Lady Churchill dead at seven o'clock that morning, "having died in her sleep some hours before of syncope from heart disease." According to Sir James, the Queen, while clearly shocked and grieving when finally told, "took it well and was none the worse" (Reid, 1987, p. 199).

p 127–128 25 December *"Did not have a good night, was very restless, & every remedy that was tried failed in making me sleep. Then when I wished to get up I fell asleep again, which was too provoking.—Went out with Lenchen & Beatrice about 1 & the former told me Sir J. Reid wished me to know that dear Jane Churchill had one of her bad heart attacks in the night, & that he had telegraphed for her son, as he thought very seriously of her condition. I said, 'You remember, I warned & asked her now whether it was safe for her to come as she was so ill this very time last year.' I felt anxious, and on coming home sent for Sir James, who said 'she is very ill,' so I asked if it would not be better to send at once for another lady, to which he replied 'most decidedly.'...I took a short drive with Louischen & Thora & we talked a great deal about Jane, as I was so distressed at her being so ill. Directly I returned, I again sent for Sir James, who said 'I was just coming to tell Y' Majesty all was over.' She had died this morning early, in her sleep.... I naturally was much upset & very unhappy, as dear Jane was one of my most faithful & intimate friends.—At 6 had a little service in the Drawing-room.... This has been a terribly sad Christmas for all!–"*

The entry for 26 December is one of the most poignant of any in the Journal's last volume. Lady Churchill's son, Victor, Lord Churchill—who had himself been named in honor of the Queen—arrives at Osborne on this day, reaching the Isle of Wight after an arduous passage through a fierce winter storm on the Solent. The grief-stricken Queen Victoria and Lord Churchill both struggle to maintain composure, each one straining to express a depth of gratitude to the other. The Queen disparages her own efforts: "He thanked me again & again. I could scarcely speak.—"

Sir James Reid's comment on the 25th that the Queen had taken the news of Lady Churchill's death fairly well and "was none the worse," was both unfounded and premature. According to Michaela Reid (Reid, 1987, p. 199), Queen Victoria "…had borne so much tragedy during the past months…. Death, it seemed was part of her daily life and she was growing accustomed to it, but with the demise of Lady Churchill the Queen's own will to live diminished." After the deaths of Affie and Christle, it was widely feared that the unexpected loss of Lady Churchill would indeed be the "coup de grace."

p 129–130 26 December *"I had a fair night & slept well at first, but later was rather restless…. Saw poor Victor Churchill, who was terribly distressed, as I was, too. The loss to me is not to be told. Dear Jane had been with me nearly 50 years…. He thanked me again & again. I could scarcely speak.—Had my little supper, consisting of Benger's food,* & then dictated to Thora.–"*

On the night of the 26th the Queen is "much disturbed by the mind," most likely by the loss of Jane Churchill; if so, such a reaction would further belie Reid's hasty and superficial impression of her as stoic on Christmas Day when he had broken the news of Lady Churchill's death. Perhaps Reid had only intended to imply that the Queen's condition had now become so alarming that she could scarcely decline any further and still sustain life.

The Queen herself acknowledged feeling "very low & sad" on the 27th, another of the infrequent occasions in the Journal's final volume where she explicitly uses the terms "sad" or "melancholy." Although her grief for Albert had been central to her subsequent life as a widow, Albert had been mourned differently. After the initial shock of his death, Queen Victoria had idealized and memorialized him, grimly determined to follow his dictates for the rest

---

* Benger's food was a floury substance which made a paste when mixed with broth or warm milk; it was used as a caloric and nutritional supplement for elderly or edentulous persons.

of her life. From this vow she seemed to gain strength, presenting herself for decades more as a person weighed down with heavy responsibilities, joyless and careworn, than as one who was conventionally grieving. But with the deaths of Affie, Christle, and now Lady Churchill coming so closely upon each other, it is as if the Queen has become too weak to resist ordinary sadness. So, at the end of her life, Queen Victoria is finally felled by grief. She now trends toward a more unrestrained sorrow, of a kind not seen since the months immediately following Albert's death 40 years earlier.

At the close of the 27 December entry, however, she mentions that she has dictated a letter to Beatrice to be sent to Vicky, attempting to reassure the dying Empress that her own physical condition has at least stabilized ("nothing to cause you alarm") and that she is coping as well as she can with Jane Churchill's death. But this letter, nearly the last she will ever write to Vicky, leaves an unmistakable impression of onrushing descent, and even the gift for which she thanks her daughter, a "tasteful" magnifying glass, only emphasizes her disabling loss of sight.

The letter dated 27 December 1900 from the Queen to the Empress Frederick, as dictated to Princess Beatrice, follows here (Ramm, 1990, p. 258):

I must dictate these few lines to you as I am not well able to write myself, and wish to thank you for your last dear letters. I am so delighted that you are pleased with my gifts and that you are a little less suffering.* A thousand thanks for the most beautiful and tasteful magnifying glass which I shall always use in thinking of you. I have

---

* Vicky, the Empress Frederick, was not, as the Queen hoped, "less suffering." She was dying in excruciating pain at Friedrichshof, her country estate. Only a short time before, the Empress had written more openly to her own daughter: "My legs are shrunken and fallen away to nothing, a mere skeleton. The agony is as bad as ever, the nights are a torture. In 24 hours I do not get 2 hours sleep. The pain is too frequent, too violent, like ever so many razors driven into my back. The tears and groans all night long drive me utterly mad. I often

not been very well myself, but nothing to cause you alarm and I have not a bad pulse. I have also been able to get out a little most days. This Christmas has been one of the saddest I ever remember, excepting '61,* and you are I am sure as horrified as I am at the loss of my good beloved Jane Churchill, who died in her sleep on Christmas Day. What her loss is to me I cannot describe or even realize yet, and that it should happen here is too sad, but it is I think what she would have wished, excepting for the trouble and sorrow it has caused. Poor Lenchen, Christian and their children have borne up wonderfully, but poor Christian is terribly aged.... As your sisters have written to you and given the very uninteresting news from here, I will end for today, hoping to be able to write myself next time.

p 130–131 27 December *"Had only a pretty good night, as I was much disturbed by the mind, I took several draughts & then some milk & fell asleep towards morning, so did not get up till nearly 1.—Felt very low & sad. There had been a service in the Chapel at 11.... Dear Jane's remains had rested there since yesterday evening.... Rested...had some broth.... Felt very sad, & saw poor Victor Churchill again. I was able to be a little calmer & talk about the happy old days.—Later I dictated to Beatrice a letter for dear Vicky & then my Journal again to Thora.... They are all overworked.—"*

The Queen continues to grieve for Lady Churchill. A "bad night" on the 27th is filled with worry about the safe transport of Lady Churchill's body across the blustery Solent. All does proceed smoothly in that operation, but the Queen, remarkable for her, and therefore significant, again accepts that

---

think I should put an end to myself if only I could. Oh, I cannot bear it any longer! Pity me! I do not think anyone can suffer much more" (Packard, 1998, p. 308).

* Prince Albert died on 14 December, 1861, at Windsor Castle.

she is feeling "low & sad." She is too weakened and depressed to dissemble or minimize.

As for the unfortunate Lady Churchill, Princess Louise recognized "how the dear lady would hate causing any disturbance ...." (Reid, 1987, p. 1990).

p 131 28 December *"I had a bad night, though I got a little sleep at the beginning. Besides I don't think I could have slept as there was such a fearful storm. Then I thought of what would be going on, beloved Jane being taken away & all following to the ship. The weather was so tempestuous, that I got alarmed about it. I went to sleep again, after I had rushed to get up, which was very tiresome.... I felt very low & sad, which distressed my children very much. Everybody seemed very sad, but said all had gone off well. My beloved old friend's remains had reached Cornbury...the funeral does not take place till tomorrow.—I had a very distressed letter from Louise, as dear Jane was her dearest friend, to whom she always turned for advice.—I took Benger's food for my supper & dictated to Thora.–"*

On 29 December the Queen reports that she ate, and even enjoyed, some solid nourishment—not her usual Benger's food—this development an anomaly, certainly, and one meriting special notice.

Relieved to hear that Lady Churchill's remains had successfully crossed the Solent, she then refers to her depression by name, using that particular word for the only time in the entire final volume of her Journal. We cannot know precisely what the Queen intended to convey on the 29th by her word-choice, and she immediately thereafter dilutes its impact by claiming that she is "rather better than yesterday," but it is fair to say that "depression" denotes in her mind serious levels of apathy and sadness: "I was very depressed...."

p 132–133 29 December *"...A fair night & I got up rather earlier, but could take little breakfast.—Went out after 1, with Lenchen & Beatrice.—Managed to eat a little cold beef, which was the first I have had for weeks, & I really enjoyed. . . . Heard from Victor Churchill all had gone off well.—I was very depressed, though rather better than yesterday.—Did some signing & dictated a letter to Bertie.—. . . Beatrice & Arthur came up after dinner & sat a little while with me.–"*

The Queen's world continues to contract as the year comes to a close. On 30 December this once admirably energetic woman starts the day very slowly after an unrestful night and does not get out until three in the afternoon. She writes that she "managed" to sign a few documents, implying that she has had to struggle against lack of energy, poor concentration, and low vision, just to attend to this most routine of the Sovereign's functions.

p 133 30 December *"Did not have a good night, though I usually sleep a little at first.—Got up too late to go out in the morning, so only took a drive after 3 with Lenchen & Beatrice.—I managed to sign a few things, & Harriet P. read to me.–. . .Afterwards dictated to Thora, & Ismay Southampton,* who kindly came, read to me, & I fell asleep.—Arthur & Louischen came to me for a little while after dinner.–"*

The next day's entry is dated 31 December, but it may have been written down the next morning, since the Queen reports that having fallen asleep, she did not write in the Journal nor dictate to Princess Thora in the evening, as was her custom.

In this entry she summarizes, succinctly enough but more devastatingly than she has ever done, the restless nighttime sleep and frustrating disruptions of her days: "The same unfortunate alternations of sleep & restlessness, so that I again did not get up when I wished to &, which

---

* Ismania, Baroness Southampton, was a Lady of the Bedchamber to Queen Victoria for various periods from 1878 to 1901.

spoilt my morning & day." It had been, indeed, "a terribly Stormy night" in every sense.*

Queen Victoria mentions here that she has named the capable and reliable naval officer Prince Louis of Battenberg, brother of Beatrice's Liko and husband of her granddaughter Victoria of Hesse, as Trustee of her personal fortune. She does not make explicit her reasons for doing so, but this act would presuppose at least some reflection on her own mortality. It was time to assure that her affairs were in order.

p 134 31 December *"A terribly Stormy night.—The same unfortunate alternations of sleep & restlessness, so that I again did not get up when I wished to &, which spoilt my morning & day.—Got out a little after 1 with Beatrice.— When I came in I had to sign for a new Trustee to my private money, who is Louis Battenberg.... The afternoon was wet, & I took a short drive in a closed carriage with Harriet P.—Rested, when I came in.—At a little after 9, after having my supper of Benger's food, Harriet P. read to me, & I fell quite asleep, so that Thora did not write the Journal, as it had got too late.... The news from S. Africa was not very good. A post of our troops had been rushed by the enemy...."*

---

* Author's note: During the Queen's last weeks of life an impressive measure of space in the Journal is given over to complaints about her inability to sleep and its deleterious effects; references to insomnia become especially prominent in the Journal entries at Osborne in December. On the last day of 1900, Queen Victoria describes her sleep difficulties of the preceding night in a similar vein, but here she begins with a terse description of the winter storm that had been raging over the Solent: "A terribly Stormy night."

For once, however, Princess Beatrice's consistently legible school-girlish handwriting failed me. As a result, I first misread "Stormy night" as "Starry night" (perhaps an unwitting association to the eponymous Van Gogh painting), but quickly realized that "Starry night" fit neither the season nor the sentiment. I next determined the writing to say "Staring night." That seemed a more fitting description of the special distress caused by insomnia, evincing not only the experience of unwanted wakefulness, but also more generally, the affliction of late-life depression. After discovering my errors, I was still struck by the aptness and poetry of "Staring night," and it then became the title of the present book.

The first of January 1901 is a milestone date: a new year and a new century. For the ailing Queen Victoria it is a most inauspicious beginning, as she well appreciates, and she offers up a typically honest self-appraisal: "Another year begins & I am feeling so weak & unwell that I enter upon it badly...."

The wintry weather—stormy lately, and on this particular day, dark and foggy—has all along been providing a background synchronous with depression. In the afternoon the Queen makes one of the last public appearances of her long reign, visiting convalescent soldiers from the South African front. Somehow she steels herself sufficiently to be able to deploy for her last public engagement the solemnity and dignity she usually displays on such occasions, but this time it must be at great cost to her.

At the end of the entry, she reports that she has taken "a little" more food in the last three days. Actually, this not-very-reassuring statement manages only to emphasize how small her nutritional intake has lately become.

p 141 1 January, 1901 *"Another year begins & I am feeling so weak & unwell that I enter upon it badly.... The same sort of night as I have been having lately, but I did get rather more sleep & was up earlier. A very dark, foggy morning.— Lenchen & Beatrice came & wished me a happy new year, as did also Thora, the others I saw later.—Heaps of telegrams, letters & cards, which Lenchen & Beatrice kindly answered for me.—In the afternoon I drove with Arthur & Thora, & we went down to the Soldiers Home where there are convalescents from S. Africa. I said a few words to them, thanking them for their services & wishing them a happy new year.... Have been able to take a little more food the last three days.–"*

On 2 January, after another "provoking" night, the Queen receives Lord Roberts. Queen Victoria deeply admires Lord Roberts for his crucial role in turning the tide of the South African conflict despite the many reversals and long casualty lists of the war: There are three thousand dead by the beginning of 1901 (Packard, 1995). At this moment Roberts is about to be replaced by General Lord Kitchener. Having lost his only son, Frederick, in the relief of Ladysmith, the usually taciturn Roberts now appears to be feeling genuine compassion for the Queen in her mourning of Christle: "Ld Roberts spoke with such grief of dear Christle's death...."

In an imaginative gesture, the Queen not only advances Roberts to an earldom, she additionally specifies "the remainder to his daughter." Without such a provision, and lacking a male heir after the death of his son, Lord Roberts' new earldom would automatically become extinct upon his death. On Lord Roberts the Queen also bestows a Garter knighthood, an honor usually reserved for members of the Royal family. She records that her recognition "quite overcame him," but it was plainly a moment of high emotion for her as well.

p 141–144 2 January *"Rather a better night, but slept late into the morning, which is so provoking.... Heard that Ld Roberts' ship had arrived safely.... I received him warmly shaking hands with him, & he knelt down & kissed my hand.... Ld Roberts spoke with such grief of dear Christle's death & said he could not say how deeply he mourned him & how he felt for all of us. Ld Roberts spoke... also of all the difficulties our army had had to contend with. He deeply deplored the loss of so many valuable lives. He still wears his arm in a sling, the result of a fall from his horse.... I then gave Ld Roberts the Garter, which quite overcame him.... I also told him I was going to confer an Earldom on him, with the remainder to his daughter.... I felt a little tired, so rested & slept for a while.—Later Ismay S. came & read to me.–"*

On 3 January, after the emotion of the New Year and the meeting with Lord Roberts, Queen Victoria has retreated to the minimal activity level of her recent baseline—a late start, some *pro forma* State business, a "little supper" for which she has no appetite, this before being read to by Harriet Phipps and dictating the day's Journal entry to Thora.

p 144–145 3 January *"I had a rather better night, though some broken sleep & was not up & dressed till 12.... Saw Sir A. Bigge about some War Office affairs.—I had not much appetite.... After I had had my little supper, Harriet P. came for ½ an hour & read to me, after which I dictated the Journal to Thora.–"*

The Queen writes, awkwardly and ungrammatically, on 4 January that she had taken "less draughts" on the night of the 3rd. The "draughts" to which she refers are probably either Trional or chlorodyne, the latter a vestigial form of the sedative-hypnotic drug chloral hydrate, prescribed by Sir James Reid. As a general indication of how critical things really are at this point—it is often difficult to recognize more explicitly from the Queen's choice of words—the slightly reduced level of medication needed to induce sleep has become her latest definition of a "better night." However, she implies that the "draughts," belatedly taking hold, themselves contributed to her sleeping late into the morning on the 4th. The desired sequence of restful nighttime sleep and daytime alertness seems to be beyond her reach.

The Queen also mentions her poor vision, which she calls "very tiresome," no doubt referring to the inconvenience and loss of independence involved in having to rely on others, principally a bored and resentful Princess Beatrice, to read newspapers and state documents to her. Then, too, she remains "uncomfortable" as the day goes on, "uncomfortable" being a frequently-used designation that in her muted vocabulary of complaints implies severe pain. The sources of the pain are again most likely her knees and back, and the discomfort is probably worse than might be assumed from her words. Her days of independent ambulation are long past.

On 4 January, Sir James Reid writes a reassuring letter to Marie Mallet from Osborne. It seems that many in the Household have found themselves drawn to Marie, a person both sensible and compassionate, whose reverence for the throne and genuine love for the Queen herself must have been apparent to all. However, if intended to reassure, Sir James's letter to Marie is unconvincing and reads now, even with the caveats he includes, as largely unfounded, considering the present condition of the Queen.

Perhaps the ordinarily cautious Sir James, like so many others, was himself suffering from a lapse in his normally solid judgement, unable to fathom the imminent loss of the Queen whose faith in him had transformed his life. Another possibility is that by writing in this vein, Reid was intentionally attempting to calm the anxiety around the Sovereign, trying to lower expectations gently, using as his vehicle the influential Mrs. Mallet. Perhaps the most likely explanation, the only one for which there is actual evidence in the letter, is that the overworked Sir James had himself racked up a serious sleep deficit and was greatly in need of respite. Reid had apparently been hoping that Sir Francis Laking, in whose skill he had little confidence, could somehow manage to spell him with sufficient competence to allow him rest and the opportunity to attend to Susan, his own temporarily ailing (and pregnant) wife. However, Sir James has not entirely lost his powers of discernment, and weighs in against the absurdity of planning a spring vacation for the Queen, considering her condition.

In his letter, Sir James also refers to the "grace-and-favor" residence at Windsor he and Susan had been assigned by the Queen. This gesture was not motivated by gratitude or magnanimity, as the Queen, for all her stirring expressions of closeness to servants and Household members, had in her actions been largely oblivious to the personal goals and basic comforts of those who served her. In fact, Her Majesty's angry outburst upon first hearing the news of Reid's engagement to Susan Baring betrayed her fear of losing his exclusive attention.

Another example of the Queen's insensitivity was her longstanding indulgence in a cultish and simplistic preference for cool temperatures, forbidding fires in the bitter November chill of Balmoral despite the hardship it may have caused to others; similarly, she was unconcerned about the effect on others of the general boredom and tedium of her Court. Thus, the grace-and-favor gesture to the Reids should be interpreted as evidence that Her Majesty now felt the need for her trusted physician to be accessible at all times, and as further corroboration that she understood the tenuousness of her hold on life. In the event, Queen Victoria was never to return to Windsor alive.

Sir James' letter of 4 January to Marie Mallet warrants being reproduced here in its entirety (Mallet, 1968, p. 221). The letter to Marie Mallet is followed by an excerpt from Sir James' letter of 2 December to the Prince of Wales (Reid, 1987, p. 197), with brief introductory and explanatory notes, and then by the Queen's own Journal entry for 4 January.

Dear Mrs. Mallet,

Just a line to tell you that the Queen is now much better. She has continued to improve ever since she consented to be treated as an invalid; and she now causes me no present anxiety. How far she may still improve it is impossible to say at her age: but I hope she may continue her invalid habits for some time longer, and so give herself every chance.

I am still of the opinion that the foreign trip would be a somewhat risky undertaking, but we shall see a few weeks hence.

I have had rather an anxious time and have been very closely tied: so H.M. is to give me a little chance of air and exercise, and Sir F. Laking is coming here for a week or so. But I am told I am still to stay here and not in May Cottage which seems to me very unnecessary! However it may yet be altered.

Susan is in bed with a feverish chill and rheumatism but otherwise she is all right. I have been very little with her since she came, so I am longing for Sir F. Laking's arrival! You may have heard that Susan is to have a small house at Windsor Castle—a great boon for us.

With kindest regards and wishing you and yours every happiness for the New Year.

Yours very sincerely,
James Reid

A more direct, less equivocal statement of the Queen's poor prognosis can be found in Reid's letter to the Prince of Wales written slightly more than one month earlier, on 2 December. One might think that Reid would be more guarded in his language in a letter to the Prince than to Mrs. Mallet, but in this earlier letter, according to Michaela Reid, the Queen's chief physician had a clear purpose; he felt that the Prince of Wales, influenced as he had been by Sir Francis Laking's false reassurances, did not yet perceive the true gravity of the Queen's condition. Reid was determined that the Prince should have the truth about the probability that the Queen would never regain her previous level of functioning, and he felt strongly that the heir to the throne should be prepared for the medical crisis that was not only inevitable, but could occur at any time.

Accordingly, in the 2 December letter, Sir James had included the following:

Since Your Royal Highness was here, the Queen's condition has materially improved in all essential respects, but still she is not what she was before, and I begin to fear that her health may remain permanently on a lower plane than hitherto. She... is feebler generally than she used to be, her voice is weaker, and her nervous system is a good deal shaken. I am very doubtful whether, at her age, they may regain their former level.... . In the course of nature this must be progressive, though with constant care and attention I trust it may be slow. Of course there is, in addition, always present the risk of some sudden illness which would be very serious at the Queen's age and in her enfeebled state.

No one save Sir James Reid was in a position to explain the situation plainly to the Prince of Wales. In referring to the "risk of some sudden illness," Reid appears to be alerting the Prince specifically to the Queen's vulnerability to stroke, given her "enfeebled state" and the episodes of aphasia and apathy that have thus far gone unmentioned. Though diplomatic, Reid was known for his truthfulness, and the high esteem in which he was held by the Queen was also widely acknowledged. He alone was able to reassure her and at times distract her with humor. Although he had at first occupied an anomalous position in the Court, not exactly a servant yet not quite a full member of the Household with privileges to dine with this group, the awkwardness was soon rectified as he rose up the ranks. Reid had been offered a knighthood, but held out a few more years for the Baronetcy he received in 1898.

At this point Queen Victoria herself reports in her entry for 4 January that she is feeling "so weary and tired." Altogether, this entry epitomizes the condition of an aging woman, now suffering from low vision, chronic musculoskeletal pain and other disabilities, and very much also from the consequences of depression, particularly insomnia and anorexia. Still, she soldiers on as Sovereign, demonstrating that she still cares very much about

Lord Roberts's reception in London and about news from the front in South Africa.

p 145–146 4 January *"Had a better night & took less draughts, but still unfortunately I slept longer than I wished.... Wished Christian, Thora & Louie good bye, Lenchen stays with us for the present. A fine afternoon, but rather hazy.... I see so badly, which is very tiresome.—Heard by telegram that Ld Roberts' reception in London yesterday, had gone off extremely well, though the weather had been dull.—Had a telegram from Ld Kitchener, which was satisfactory.—I spent rather an uncomfortable afternoon, & felt so weary & tired.–..."*

On 5 January Sir Francis Laking arrived at Osborne to allow Reid a brief respite, but the Queen refused to see him, to the great irritation of Sir James's wife. As noted several generations later by Michaela Reid, "Jamie" was alone, with the sole exception of Marie Mallet, in his awareness of the precariousness of the Queen's condition. Despite Sir James's attempts to convey his concern, the message did not fully register. The Prince of Wales, the trio of Princesses on the scene (Christian, Louise, and Beatrice), the Queen's Personal Secretary, Harriet Phipps, and many others, were all at this time clinging to the unlikely prospect of Her Majesty traveling to France or Italy in the spring. In part, they may have been attempting to uphold the familiar timetable of the *ancien régime* because they, especially the Princesses, realized that they would face a loss of rank and relevance in the succeeding reign. (Behind the scenes Household members sarcastically referred to the three Princesses as "the petticoats.")

On 5 January a furious Susan Reid complained to her husband about Dr. Laking's ineffectiveness and about the prevailing disinclination of the Royal family to accept the reality of the Queen's deteriorating condition (Reid, 1987, pp. 199–200):

Laking's visit at Osborn [sic] is a great fraud! and does not relieve Jamie of any of his work! The Queen will not see him! at least not about her health, and she can hardly bear Jamie out of her sight! She...has ups and downs and gets very easily over tired, and when so, she gets into a nervous depressed hopeless state. However...her family and Miss Phipps will insist (in spite of Jamie's opinion!!) on thinking her much better than she is and it is all he can do to prevent them overtiring her, by too much talking. The only difference Laking's visit has made is that Jamie was able to dine here twice. Last night he was to do so again but the Queen was in a nervous mood, so he gave it up, and she was so pleased and so grateful!! She does depend on him entirely now.... As things are at present Jamie thinks it is out of the question that the Queen should go abroad.... However, the family and Miss Phipps are still in favor of it, but I think gradually they will see for themselves that it is impossible.

The Queen's own entry for 5 January, laconic and uninformative as it is, nevertheless underscores the reasons for Sir James's anxiety.

p 146 5 January *"Had a bad & much disturbed night. Felt very exhausted. Beatrice went out with me for a short while late in the morning & in the afternoon I drove with Lenchen.... It was very fine, but cold. I was very drowsy, when I came home.—Harriet P. read to me.–"*

The Queen finally did allow Sir Francis Laking to see her on 6 January. There is no record of this encounter, but 10 days later (i.e., on 16 January, three days after the Journal's last entry on 13 January), Reid describes in his notes how Laking had been misled by the Queen to conclude that she was much better than she in fact was (Reid, 1987, p. 201; Abrams, 2015):

I asked her to see Laking, as he was going away the next day, and she said yes, and I got the maids to remind her. Accordingly at 8 he was sent for, I having told him about the Q's dazed condition. And at 8.45 as I was going down to dinner I met him coming back, and to my surprise he told me the Queen was all right, that she had been speaking to him for ¾ hour on a great many topics and was quite herself, in fact he did not believe she was as bad as I thought. I told him it was only an instance of how wonderfully she could pull herself together when she saw anyone but her maids or me, and that I should not wonder if she were quite confused again after he left. 10 minutes later I was sent for by the maids and found H.M. quite exhausted as confused as ever. She went back to bed at once....

Meanwhile, Vicky's health has continued to be a worrying preoccupation for the Queen. The Empress Frederick's diagnosis of cancer and its inoperable state had first been confirmed during her visit to Balmoral in the autumn of 1898, at which time the Prince of Wales and Princess Beatrice were undoubtedly told (Packard, 1998). How much information about Vicky's diagnosis and terrible prognosis was revealed to Queen Victoria at that time is uncertain, but, as in so many other matters of importance, Her Majesty seems to know.

Perhaps in one of her clearer moments, the Queen now decides to write her letter of 6 January to the Empress Frederick in her own hand rather than dictate it to Thora or Beatrice as she had been doing recently for most of her personal correspondence. The significance of this is clear enough: Well aware that Vicky had been disliked in Germany, both for her English origins and her liberal politics, the Queen felt a need for the utmost secrecy and wrote in this way to keep the indiscreet Beatrice and even trustworthy Thora from knowing the full extent of Vicky's illness.

Whatever the reason, penning the message to Vicky by herself required great concentration and will, considering her compromised physical and mental state and failing vision. The Queen's determination to do this could reflect her desire to live, to overcome, but the special effort also suggests Queen Victoria's recognition that this might be her last letter to Vicky. Therefore, the breezy tone with which that she says she must "end for today to save the post" is not casual at all, but a calculated attempt to attenuate the overwhelming feeling of the moment. Still, this final message concludes with a salvo of emotion, a last expression of love, Empress to Empress, dying mother to dying daughter: "God bless you, darling child" (Ramm, 1990, pp. 258–259).

Osborne 6 January 1901

> I am so grieved to see by your dear letters that your hands trouble you so. It is very troublesome [that they] hurt you so much. I attempt to write myself. I don't suffer from my eyes, only the sight is rather bad since I have been rather poorly but I hope it will soon be much better. I gave your message to Lord Roberts who was greatly gratified. There were great crowds to receive him and both Beatrice and Arthur went out to receive him. He is looking well and was greatly gratified. Then I gave him the Garter and told him that he was to be an earl.... I must, I fear, end for today to save the post. God bless you, darling child.

The Queen's own Journal entry for 6 January once more acknowledges, again significantly, that she is "sad."

p 147–147 6 January *"An improved night, though I awoke often.... The accounts of Vicky are not at all satisfactory, which makes me so sad.—* It blew so hard & was so cold, that I did not go out in the morning.—Saw Sir Francis Laking, who is here to relieve Sir James Reid a little.–"*

Queen Victoria's entry for 7 January describes an ordinary day for Her Majesty—ordinary, anyway, according to her present standard. She has her usual late start followed by a drive, this time requiring a closed carriage because of the high wind. Then her attention turns to family matters. In the early evening she is read aloud to, eats something—surely not much—for dinner, and lastly listens to reports from the front sent by Lord Kitchener. Perhaps a respite from the high emotion of recent days is being sought.

p 147–148 7 January *"Had a much better night, but still slept late.—A very cold day with a very high wind.—Took a short drive in a closed carriage.... Dictated some letters to Lenchen.—We were delighted to hear from Anna Battenberg,† also from Victoria B. & finally, officially, that the young Queen of Italy is at length going to have a child.... Ismay S. read to me in the evening out of the new book by Lᵞ Margaret Makenzie called the 'Mystery of Rougemount.' After dinner... further reports from Lᵈ Kitchener.–"*

Over the next two days, 8 and 9 January, the Queen continues to weaken, complaining of extreme fatigue following two terrible nights, the first one "restless" and the next one simply "bad." On the 9th, however, in another of the considerate gestures of the kind that endeared Queen Victoria to those around her, if not to the nation as a whole, she appoints Verena,

---

* Vicky, The Empress Frederick, died on 5 August 1901, less than seven months after the death of her mother Queen Victoria on 22 January 1901.

† Anna, née Princess of Montenegro (1874–1971), was the wife of Prince Francis Joseph of Battenberg and sister-in-law to Prince Henry and Prince Louis.

Lady Churchill, to the post of Verena's recently-deceased mother-in-law and intimate of the Queen, Jane Churchill.

p 148 8 January *"Had a restless night & woke very often. The ground was white with snow when I got up.... Got out in a closed car for a while with Harriet P.—I was so drowsy that I slept for 2 hours from 6 o'clock...."*

p 148–149 9 January *"A bad night, & got up late.—Did not go out till the afternoon.... It was fine & mild & all the snow was disappearing fast.—I have appointed Verena Churchill to her dear mother-in-law's place as Lady in Waiting, which keeps up the connection with our dear Jane, & I know she would have been so pleased. Verena is very amiable & nice.–"*

From 10 to 13 January the Queen begins to drift toward death.

p 149–150 10 January *"Rather a better night, but I slept...late.—Only got out for a short time in the morning...."*

p 150 11 January *"A better night, but felt very tired.—Out in the garden chair after 1, Lenchen & Beatrice walking with me.... Went as far as Barton & back. Felt so weary...slept for more than 2 hours.—Afterward Lenchen & Beatrice played duets to me, very pretty things, the 'Gondoliers,' Gounod's Ballet music from 'Faust,' etc.–"*

p 151 12 January *"Had a good night & could take some breakfast better.—There was a dense fog & no ships could cross.... Harriet read to me after my supper & Lenchen & Beatrice came up afterwards.–"*

p 151–152 13 January *"Had a fair night, but was a little wakeful. Got up earlier and had some milk.—Lenchen came & read some papers.—Out before 1,* *in the garden chair, Lenchen & Beatrice going with me.—Rested a little, had some food & took a short drive with Lenchen & Beatrice.—Rested when I came in & at 5:30, went down to the Drawing Room, where a short service was held, by M*^{r}*. Clement Smith, who performed it so well, & it was a great comfort to me.—Rested again afterwards, then did some signing & dictated to Lenchen.—"*

The Journal closes abruptly here with the following entry in Princess Beatrice's hand:

"This is the last entry into the Queen's Journal before her death on Jan:22$^{nd.}$*."*

References

Abrams, R. (2015). Sir James Reid and the death of Queen Victoria. *The Gerontologist, 55*(6), 943–950. https://doi.org/10.1093/geront/gnu016

Mallet, V. (Ed.). (1968). *Life with Queen Victoria: Marie Mallet's letters from court, 1887–1901.* Houghton Mifflin Company: Boston, MA, p. 221.

Packard, J.M. (1995). *Farewell in splendor: The passing of Queen Victoria and her age.* Dutton (The Penguin Group): New York, NY, p. 9.

Packard, J.M. (1998). *Victoria's daughters.* St. Martin's Griffin: New York, NY, pp. 299, 308.

Ramm, A. (Ed.). (1990). *Beloved & darling Child: Last letters between Queen Victoria & her eldest daughter, 1896–1901.* Sutton Publishing: Stroud, UK, pp. 258–259.

Reid, M. (1987). *Ask Sir James: The life of Sir James Reid, personal physician to Queen Victoria.* Eland Books: London, UK, pp. 195, 197, 199, 199–120, 201.

Victoria, R.I. (1900–1901). *Queen Victoria's Journal (Royal Archives), 18 December, 1900–13 January, 1901,* pp. 122–152.

6.　Death of the Queen (13–22 January 1901)

From Queen Victoria's last Journal entry on 13 January 1901 until her death on 22 January, what is known of the course her illness is derived largely from Sir James Reid's detailed notes. Unlike the majority of his documents dealing with Queen Victoria that Sir James had specifically instructed were to be burned after he died, the diary of these critical January days was spared from the flames, perhaps inadvertently, and subsequently preserved in the original scrapbooks by his descendants.

This account of Queen Victoria's last days follows the day-by-day format and content of Reid's scrapbook diary, but his notes are re-interpreted here from a contemporary medical-psychiatric perspective.

The subtitles used for each time period are phrases taken from Sir James' surviving notes.

13–14 January: *"Queen was rather childish and apathetic."*

On 13 January Sir James Reid [see Reid, 1987, pp. 200–213, for all James Reid citations below] wrote: "Queen was rather childish and apathetic." This observation, pointing to a frank confusional state, calls into question the authenticity not only of what was supposedly dictated by the Queen for her Journal on that day, but also of the entries dating back a month or more. It is likely, considering Queen Victoria's cognitive, emotional and physical deterioration, that many of the late entries were partly or wholly fabricated by Princess Beatrice, who assumed responsibility for editing the Journal after Her Majesty's death. It can be safely assumed that Beatrice, with the Queen's legacy in mind, engaged in a process of editing and rewriting in a manner that would uphold her mother's dignity and provide more consistency and coherence than could be expected from the fragmented thoughts of a dying individual. Copying and revising her mother's Journal was to occupy Princess Beatrice for decades. Beatrice was better suited to this task than the Queen's other surviving children, having taken down some of the original entries by herself by dictation when Princess Thora was unavailable.

Princess Beatrice, the youngest of Victoria and Albert's children, had fulfilled the traditional sacrificial role of the youngest daughter by devoting her own life, at least a substantial part of it, to the roles of companion, helper and confidant to her aging mother. Her discomfort with this position had intermittently been a source of conflict between mother and daughter. But, as noted earlier, the original standoff around her marriage had ended with a compromise in which Beatrice was allowed to marry, with the proviso that she and her future family would make Osborne their permanent home; even her honeymoon with Liko Battenberg entailed only a brief stay at a property on the Isle of Wight a short distance from the main house. In the years after her own husband died in 1895, Beatrice had become ever more indispensable to the Queen and had therefore been the principal firsthand witness, aside from Sir James Reid, of Her Majesty's physical and mental decline. In addition, Princess Beatrice was a competent wordsmith in her own right, having in 1891 published her own English translation from the original German of *The Adventures of Count George Albert of Erbach* by Emil Kraus.

It is possible that in her editing and rewriting, Princess Beatrice extended the Journal's final entries to the date of 13 January to coincide with the unequivocal end of the Queen's ability to dictate letters or conduct business. In the event, Her Majesty's meeting with Lord Roberts on the

14th had to be quietly concluded when it became apparent that, at least transiently aphasic, she was unable to speak. Thus ended Queen Victoria's last official activity as Sovereign.

15 January: *"Cerebral degeneration."*

The following day, 15 January, Queen Victoria's eyes were examined by the eminent German ophthalmologist Hermann Pegenstecher, a professor from Wiesbaden who had treated the Queen previously at Windsor, using belladonna to induce pupillary dilation around her cataracts. This procedure, repeated on several occasions, had as expected provided only temporary relief. Professor Pegenstecher was widely known for the then-innovative technique of intracapsular cataract extraction, but the Queen had been unable to bring herself to "go under the knife," fearing, not unreasonably, that in so doing she could risk what little remained of her vision.

A detailed description of what Dr. Pegenstecher found in that fundoscopic examination on 15 January did not survive, but there is no doubt that it had been the underlying microvascular pathology that was of present interest and no longer the cataracts *per se*. These signs of cerebrovascular disease revealed in the fundoscopic examination represented the advanced stages of malignant hypertension, and possibly other chronic pathological processes as well.

The fundoscopic findings were important because Sir James Reid was by this time seeking an explanation for the latest changes in the Queen's mental status. According to Sir James, Dr. Pegenstecher felt that the

cataract was little worse but [he] confirmed my opinion (for many weeks) of cerebral degeneration.... During the past few days the Queen's disposition had quite altered; nothing annoyed her and she took apathetically things that formerly would have irritated her. When she woke from sleep in her room, she was not able for some time to realize where she was.

The acute changes in alertness observed by Sir James on 15 January might have reflected new neuropathology in the frontal lobe, and perhaps also elsewhere in the brain, replacing melancholia with apathy. However, it would be consistent with contemporary models of late-life depression to infer that the "cerebral degeneration" that was now obvious had, in retrospect, played a determining role in the development of the Queen's depressed state emerging at the end of the summer. These brain changes had probably been advancing quietly over a period of years, before either cognitive or mood symptoms were evident, providing a biological substrate for the mounting weight of misfortune and grief.

It is also possible that some of the clinical *consequences* of depression, such as exhaustion and malnutrition, could themselves have been exacerbating factors for the accumulation of cerebrovascular pathology that reached a critical threshold in December and January. In all likelihood these developments had for some time been proceeding in *both* directions—neuropathological changes favoring depression, and depression favoring further neuropathological changes via exhaustion and malnutrition—together culminating in a new phase of apathy and delirium.

16 January: *"Dazed, confused, and aphasic."*

On the 16th, Reid observed a continuation of the same sleep-cycle disturbance that had plagued the Queen for months—awake for most of the night, dozing throughout the day—but now with the alarming new aspects of aphasia and fluctuating levels of alertness. He wrote that the Queen had rather a disturbed night, but was very drowsy all forenoon, and disinclined to get up, although she kept saying in a semi-confused way that she must get up. I saw her asleep in bed in the forenoon, as I was rather anxious about her, and the maids said she was too drowsy to notice me. This was the first time I had ever seen the Queen when she was in bed. She was lying on her right side huddled up and I was struck by how small she appeared.

Remarkably, Reid had never before been allowed to see the Queen in bed in 20 years, let alone perform anything close to a physical examination. (In that respect she could as well have been Katherine of Aragon, the first of Henry VIII's wives, who deemed it improper to be examined by the excellent Arabic physicians who had arrived from Spain to attend her and who might have helped her avert some of her many miscarriages). The Queen had in fact permitted hands-on medical supervision in the past, but only for her confinements; in this regard the births of her last two children, Prince Leopold in 1853 and Princess Beatrice in 1857, broke new ground, introducing the practice of inhaling chloroform for anesthesia.

That day (16 January), anticipating Queen Victoria's impending death, Reid decided that it had become urgent to inform senior members of the Royal family, the Royal Household, and the Government of the critical situation as he saw it. Sir James presented the Queen's unfavorable prognosis to the Princesses Christian and Beatrice in person, speaking as plainly as possible to avoid any misunderstanding of his message. Covering himself, he also sent confidential notes to the Heir Apparent to the throne, the Prince of Wales; to his son, the Duke of York, the second heir; to Fritz Ponsonby, the Queen's Assistant Private Secretary, who with the Private Secretary was responsible for informing the Government of the death or incapacity of the Sovereign; and to Sir Richard Douglas Powell, another of the Queen's Physicians-in-Ordinary.

At 7.30 that evening Reid saw the Queen again and found her "dazed, confused, and aphasic."

17 January: *"Precarious but not hopeless."*

The next morning, the 17th, the Queen was "very confused, aphasic and drowsy"—similar to the previous day, but clearly worse. Reid concluded that the end must now not be far off. "I did not like her condition, and thought she might be getting comatose, and might in fact die within a few days." He immediately informed the Princesses Beatrice and Christian and sent for Sir Richard Powell to provide back-up medical support.

Reid, who saw the Queen again with Powell at 8.15 in the evening, wrote of that encounter:

> She was rather apathetic and did not pull herself together at all (for the first time) on seeing a stranger. She said nothing to him, except to answer rather incoherently the few questions he put to her. On leaving the room, Powell said to me there could be no possible doubt as to her having cerebral degeneration, and that her condition was precarious but not hopeless.

In retrospect, and perhaps as it also may have seemed in the moment, the line drawn by Dr. Powell between "precarious" and "hopeless" aimed at a level of precision that could not have existed.

Meanwhile, Reid's wife was worrying about *him*. His professional life, and to a great extent his personal life as well, had been devoted to the service of Queen Victoria. Dr. Reid had in effect exchanged professional ambition for social advancement, having all but given up his early academic interests; and the Queen's preference in her widowhood for the remote outposts of Osborne and Balmoral meant that he was unable to attend Grand Rounds and other scientific programs in London. Even when the Court was at Windsor, relatively near to London, Her Majesty's demands for Reid's immediate attention whenever she wished it, and her intolerance of substitutes, meant that he was unable to travel even short distances away from the Castle grounds.

Throughout his years with the Queen, Reid had maintained his integrity and the respect of other members of the Royal Family and courtiers. But the end of the Queen's life, and with it, a break in the existence he had known for many years, were unmistakably approaching. Also, Susan Reid suspected that her husband had seriously underestimated the strength of his attachment to the Queen. Susan wrote to Reid's mother on the 17th:

> ...If the end comes, I know it will be a wrench to him...the only consolation is that I don't think one could wish her to live in a state of childishness, which from the present state of her brain seems inevitable.

18 January: *"The right side of her face was rather flat."*

On 18 January, Reid began his entry with the observation that he found "little change from yesterday," but he then contradicted himself *volte force* by adding that now "...the articulation was bad. The right side of her face was rather flat, and the left side drooping. She slept much and was rather weak." There had certainly been another change for the worse: The Queen had had a stroke.

That evening Reid again took Powell to see the Queen with him; Powell fully shared his sense of alarm. Reid wrote of that evening visit: "I thought her intellectually rather worse, but not vegetatively," presumably referring to a decline in cognitive function without an accompanying change in alertness. However, there could be no ambiguity about the fact that cerebral damage was developing rapidly and now diffusely.

Reid continued, as discreetly and tactfully as possible, to prepare key individuals for the Queen's rapidly approaching death. Risking the anger of the Prince of Wales and the Princesses, who had been united only in their shared contempt and loathing for their eldest nephew, the Kaiser, Sir James secretly contacted Emperor Wilhelm in Germany to inform him of the Queen's condition, sending him the following telegram: "Disquieting symptoms have developed which cause considerable anxiety. This is private. Reid." He also sought to persuade the Prince of Wales, who had been falsely reassured by Sir Francis Laking and also by several baselessly hopeful letters from Princess Christian, to release a bulletin to allay public anxiety. However, the Prince, still not fully grasping the seriousness of developments, at this point planned to spend the weekend at his Sandringham estate, remote from Osborne.

19 January: *"Am I better?"*

On the 19th Reid was angrily confronted by Princess Christian for having informed the Prince of Wales by telegram that the Queen's condition was now grave. Reid had also asked that the Heir Apparent, if he did not wish to come immediately to Osborne, remain in London so that he would at least be prepared to cross the Solent on short notice. However, the three Princesses on the scene, Christian, Louise, and Beatrice, were having difficulty accepting that their august mother could actually die; and drawing from a well of resentments dating back to childhood, they did not want their brother, the Prince of Wales, at Osborne. The princesses were even more loath to deal with their troublesome nephew the Kaiser, who unbeknownst to them, was already *en route* to England. In the event, Reid stood his ground with Princess Christian, who grudgingly gave way; and the Prince of Wales, now grasping the significance of Reid's telegram, set out at once for Osborne, arriving at 5 p.m.

Regarding the arrangements made for after her death, Queen Victoria had left several memoranda written in the 1870s that included detailed instructions for a military-style funeral, but these were not revised until 1897. The revision was precipitated not by the Jubilee celebrations of that milestone year, but rather by the chaos surrounding the death of her first cousin Princess Mary Adelaide of Cambridge, the Duchess of Teck, who, to the consternation of her family, had left no will. The Queen's older set of instructions focused on the central role she intended for her servant, John Brown, who she then assumed would survive her, but by 1897 had been for many years dead. One of the original memoranda also included an ambiguous phrase which could read, depending upon one's inclination, either as straightforward or conditional, the latter interpretation suggesting that the Queen may have fancied that she would not die for a very long time, perhaps never:

> *In case* [emphasis added] of the Queen's death she wishes that her faithful and devoted personal attendant (and true friend) Brown should be in the room and near at hand, and that he should watch over her earthly remains and place it in the coffin ....

The Queen's daughters were not alone in their reluctance to accept that Her Majesty could actually die. The prospect of Queen Victoria dying after a 63-year-old reign had about it an air of unreality for many. But reality, holding nothing back, was now beginning to appear bleak. On 19 January, Reid and Powell saw the Queen together many times throughout the day. The Prince had earlier approved the first cautiously phrased bulletin, issued just before noon, informing the public of the developing crisis but beyond that revealing as little as possible: "The Queen is suffering from great physical prostration accompanied by symptoms that cause anxiety." More tellingly, it was also announced that she would "abstain for the present from transacting business."

That evening, as occurred intermittently until the end, the Queen had a brief interval of relative clarity, and Reid wrote that "I again became hopeful that she might still pull through after all, though of course still most anxious and feeling that a day or two would decide one way or the other." Short periods of alertness alternating with longer stretches of semi-consciousness were, after all, distinguishing components of encroaching delirium, and as such were recognized by Reid and Powell as unfavorable prognostic signs. But apparently Sir James held to the belief that partial recovery remained a possibility, if a remote one. So when the Queen asked him: "'Am I better? I have been very ill,' his reply: ' Yes, Y.M. has been very ill but you are now better,'" contained a small grain of truth.

Later that day the Queen asked to see Reid alone again:

> When I told her that everybody had gone out, she looked in my face and said, 'I should like to live a little longer, as I have still a few things to settle. I have arranged most things, but there are still some left, and I want to live a little longer.'

These often-quoted remarks seem to lack the Queen's distinctive style of phrasing, and are more likely to have been fashioned by Sir James than by Her Majesty, Sir James having deemed it politic to portray the dying monarch in a fearless, stoic light; or perhaps he himself was emotionally unprepared for Queen Victoria's death and preferred to see her as still bold and courageous. But the underlying sentiment, if not the choice of words, may in fact have been the Queen's. However much she may have longed to be reunited with Albert, she feared death and recoiled from it, especially the prospect of imminent death. Whether these comments were the Queen's own words recalled verbatim by Sir James or were his own creations or embellishments, they have captured the imagination of generations of biographers who have repeated them.

Sir James himself recognized the Queen's personal regard for him and faith in his abilities, but he was not so flattered as to miss the aspect of her fear of dying, and most unsettling of all, the breakdown of her consciousness of position. "She appealed to me in this pathetic way with great trust as if she thought *I* could make her live." For Reid, the person and the position of Monarch, previously bound together, were now distinct entities, the person fragile and helpless, the aura of position still present but rapidly fading.

There was to be no clarification about what exactly were the "few things to settle" that the Queen had in mind. That evening a more favorable bulletin was composed, but the moment passed quickly, and Reid concluded his personal entry for 19 January on another discouraging note: "At night the Queen was not so well again, and very weak."

19–20 January: *"Hardly ever intelligible."*

Reid stayed on with the Queen all through the night of the 19th, describing her as "very confused and restless and evidently worse." During the night she began to receive oxygen for the first time in her illness. In the morning, Reid had her moved from her large double bed to a smaller wheeled bed so that her maids could attend to her without stretching forward awkwardly. Then, during the day (20 January) "…she took food [in liquid form] fairly well, but was apathetic and aphasic, and hardly ever intelligible. Pulse 100, respiration 28."

Both Reid and Powell were again apprehensive, and throughout the day reported frequently from Osborne's recently installed telephone connection to the Prince of Wales, who had gone back to London that morning to meet the Kaiser as he arrived in England. (Greeting visiting royalty, especially a King or Queen, at the train station was a matter of routine protocol but now had additional importance as a gesture intended to allay public apprehensiveness). By the early evening, "the Queen was almost quite unconscious and had much difficulty in swallowing," reflecting the latest developments in her progressive decline in neurological status.

The second of two public bulletins for the 20th, a Sunday, was released at 4.30 in the afternoon. Its phrasing was crafted to imply that the Queen's condition had stabilized to a degree, while at the same time alerting her subjects to expect the worst in a short time: "Her Majesty's strength has been fairly maintained throughout the day. Although no fresh developments have taken place, the symptoms continue to cause anxiety."

The Queen's daughters now visited her freely, "but she recognized none of them." In the evening, anticipating that the Queen might die at any moment, Reid and Powell advised the Prince of Wales to return as quickly as possible to Osborne and to bring the Kaiser with him.

20–21 January: *"We thought she was going to 'bat' [die]."*

The night of the 20th came and went in much the same manner as the previous one. Reid, with Powell, was again with the Queen all night, watching closely and administering oxygen. "We thought she was perhaps going to die quickly, but...toward morning she rallied." The internist and cardiologist Sir Thomas Barlow (Physician Extraordinary, the courtesy title to which retired "Ordinaries" generally reverted) joined them at 10 on the morning of the 21st. As expected, Sir Thomas had nothing new to offer, but Reid and Powell were grateful for the support: "We were very glad to have him with us."

Just before noon the Queen asked for her favorite little dog, Turi, an Italian Spitz, who, though out for his walk at the moment, was eventually found. He was placed beside the Queen, "who patted him and seemed pleased...." After a while Turi became too restless to remain on the bed and was whisked away. Around this time the Kaiser, the Prince of Wales, and the Dukes of Connaught and York arrived and entered the room. The Queen, whether from confusion, poor eyesight, or both, did not recognize any of them, although a short time before, she had embraced Turi without hesitation. Decades earlier the Queen had declared, again assuming a vaguely hypothetical attitude about her own death, that she would dislike having "hordes" of relatives gathering about her, "*if* I am dying" [emphasis added].

In the afternoon, Reid took on the potentially charged task of arranging for the Kaiser, who with uncharacteristic humility had promised to say nothing to upset or excite the Queen, to take his rightful place at Her Majesty's bedside the next day, along with other members of the Royal Family. Reid's intervention on behalf of the Kaiser was an act of historical justice and also political courage, since none of the immediate relatives would likely have been willing to accept such a responsibility, notwithstanding the fact that Emperor Wilhelm was Queen Victoria's eldest grandson.

That evening, Reid brought in the Prince of Wales alone. The Queen took Reid's hand and kissed it "repeatedly," no doubt mistaking him for the Prince. Later he ushered in the Princess of Wales, whom he left alone with the Queen for a few minutes. In a hastily-written note to his wife, Reid resorted to the idiosyncratic slang of her family, the Barings, as a kind of coded communication: "Bipps [the Queen] was very bad last night, and we thought she was going to bat [die]."

21–22 January: *"Your Majesty will soon be better."*

On the night of the 21st, an exhausted Reid was up all night for the third time without interruption, sending for Powell and Barlow at intervals, but never leaving the Queen himself. He reported the Queen to be "semi-conscious," but still able to swallow. More ominously, she also had the beginning of tracheal rales* and a decreasingly "efficient" cough. She weakened further toward the morning. However, she still recognized Reid, who wrote that she "asked for me repeatedly."

At 9.30 that morning (the 22nd), when Reid had finally gone to wash and change his clothes, Powell, who had taken his place, suddenly rushed to his room and asked him to return immediately, as he thought the Queen was dying. At this point the senior family members were summoned, while Reid continued to give the Queen oxygen. The Princesses Christian, Beatrice and Louise, the Prince of Wales and the Kaiser were all present, although the Queen could not see who was there, and the Prince preferred not to tell her that the Kaiser was with them. When Reid gently suggested to the Prince that it might be better for the Queen to know of the Kaiser's presence, he replied: "No it would excite her too much." Then the Queen rallied again for a while, spoke clearly and took some food. Powell and Barlow, ever hopeful, and now genuinely moved, pronounced her vitality "phenomenal."

22 January: *"The Queen is sinking."*

Before noon, in another bold act, Reid seized the moment of the Queen's temporary rally to wrest another reversal from the Prince, now obtaining his

---

* Rales are crackling or swishing sounds created during breathing that are most readily detected using a stethoscope. They suggest the presence of fluid in the lungs or trachea.

permission to bring in the Kaiser to see his grandmother alone. Entering, Sir James addressed the Queen, using the opportunity to tell his patient something of the truth of her situation as well as ushering the Kaiser into her presence: "Your Majesty, your grandson the Emperor is here; he has come to see you as you are so ill." According to Reid's account, the Queen "smiled and understood. I went out and left him with her five minutes alone. She said to me afterwards, 'The Emperor is very kind.'"

Although he struggled to remain detached and objective while emotions ran high all around him, Reid himself was clearly affected by the spirit of the Queen, whose imminent death portended a decisive break in the only professional life and adult social milieu he had ever known. Unusually for him, Sir James then gave way momentarily to incautious optimism. In the early afternoon—the Queen was to die that evening—he wrote to Susan:

> She does not look like dying just now; and I can't help admiring her determination not to give up the struggle while she can. I hardly dare to hope she may yet win, though she deserves to.... She often smiles when she hears my voice, and says she will do 'anything I like.' The whole thing is most pathetic, and rather gives me a lump in the throat....

There was of course little that Reid could do to alter the course of events, and for days he had been struggling against his own sadness and a level of fatigue that threatened to affect his judgment. Yet, in the end, Reid's efforts to preside calmly over the fraught scene; to provide accurate, timely information; to defer to the Prince of Wales in an unspoken but unmistakable message to his siblings about his imminent change in status; and to insist that the Kaiser's rank and importance be recognized—these interventions were all recognized by the Royal family as contributions of the greatest meaning. Reid's crucial role and the exemplary manner in which he discharged it earned him much gratitude, which was spontaneously expressed by the new King and Queen, the Kaiser and other family members in the moments immediately after Queen Victoria's death. It would be justifiable to consider that Reid's creative use of his medical authority to assure a dignified death for his patient presaged the role of primary care physicians in contemporary palliative care and hospice models (Abrams, 2015).

Queen Victoria began to weaken again in the afternoon. At about 4 pm, while the rest of the family was out of the room and the Queen was being made more comfortable, in an empathic gesture, Reid advised the Prince of Wales that the Bishop of Winchester, who along with Mr. Smith of the local Whippingham parish, had been reading aloud prayers for the dying, should cease to do so until the Queen was actually dying, so as not to upset her further. This time the Prince agreed readily, and Bishop Davidson's droning recitation of *"Lead Kindly Light"* was halted. Also at 4 pm, Reid, Powell and Barlow issued a bulletin: "The Queen is sinking."

When the medical team and family, including the Kaiser, returned to the room, Reid wrote: "The Queen kept looking at me, and frequently gasped 'Sir James,' and 'I'm very ill,' and *I* each time replied, 'Your Majesty will soon be better.'"

The Queen probably knew—and with equal plausibility did not want to know—that she was dying. Queen Victoria was not among those rare humans who can "stare death in the face" undaunted. She had faced many trials during the last months of her life, but this disciplined, soldierly monarch, daughter of the martinet Duke of Kent, abhorred defeat of any kind. Even at this late hour, her self-assessment that she had been "very ill" still implied a chance of survival.

Reid himself was uncomfortable with the Queen Victoria's idealization of him, but accepted it and understood that it was driven by anxiety and desperation. Here was a spectacularly important patient, the Queen-Empress, a rare female Sovereign in her own right, only the fifth Queen Regnant in England since 1066 and quite possibly the world's greatest potentate, now attributing to Sir James Reid, the son of a country veterinarian, powers over life and death. The unstated implication was that she would recover from illness and live to reign on, if he but saw to it.

To the Queen, Reid was perhaps in need of reminders of his life-saving function, to which in her last moments she redirected him (at the same time strenuously re-orienting herself to her current reality) by repeating over and over: "I'm very ill." This aspect of the Queen's relationship with Reid was not new, but in that last hour of her life, the messages between the dying monarch and her sleep-deprived doctor, messages both spoken and unspoken, had taken on the greatest possible import to both.

As many physicians in similar circumstances have done before and since, Sir James chose to give the Queen the reassurance for which she seemed to be pleading; thus committed, he did so freely and abundantly, repeating over and over in his heavy Scottish brogue the patently false statement: "Your Majesty will soon be better." Reid appears to have felt that this was the only response he could make to the entreaties of a frightened, dying woman. He loved truth, as did the Queen herself, but it was here trumped by compassion.

Reid continues with his description of the death scene, now adding an unnecessary dramatic flourish obviously intended for posterity:

A few minutes before she died her eyes turned fixedly to the right and gazed on the picture of Christ in the [copy of Caravaggio's] 'Entombment of Christ' over the fireplace. Her pulse kept beating well till the end when she died with my arm around her.

From about 5.30 to the moment of the Queen's death at almost exactly 6.30, Reid reports that he had been kneeling at her right side with my right hand on her right pulse all this time, my left arm supporting her in a semi-upright position, helped by the Kaiser who knelt on the opposite side of the bed.... The Queen kept looking at me and saying 'Sir James' frequently.

Both Reid and the Kaiser had to have endured much discomfort, frozen as they were like bookends in their respective positions for a full hour. This was especially true for the Kaiser, who on the Queen's left side had been helping to maintain her partially raised position by balancing her weight on his only good arm, the right.* Unlike Reid, the Emperor had been unable to get any relief by shifting the weight to his other arm from time to time.

In the minutes just before Queen Victoria's last heartbeats, the family members gathered in the room had been calling out their own names, seemingly with the hope that some part of them might accompany Queen Victoria into the afterlife. As the voices of the Royal children and grandchildren rose and fell, the Queen lapsed in and out of alertness. Here are excerpts from Lytton Strachey's depiction of the monarch's last thoughts, his imaginative effort to telescope the emotional milestones of her life, in *Queen Victoria* (Strachey, 1921, pp. 423–424):

Perhaps her fading mind called up once more the shadows of the past to float before it...passing back and back...to older and ever older memories...to the spring woods at Osborne...Albert's face under the green lamp...the Archbishop of Canterbury on his knees in the dawn...a great old repeater watch of her father's in its tortoise shell case...and the trees and the grass at Kensington.

---

* Kaiser Wilhelm II had an atrophic and largely useless left arm resulting from severe injury to the brachial innervation sustained during a traumatic birth, a condition generally referred to as Erb's palsy.

Several death scene accounts report that through a haze of cataracts and confusion the Queen was able at the last to recognize her son. To the person who in a few seconds would automatically assume the prerogatives and burdens and mystique of sovereignty, the Queen may have spoken her last intelligible word, his name *en famille*, "Bertie." If so, that would symbolize the "passing of the Sceptre," if perhaps a trifle too neatly. In fact, one gets the impression from Reid's notes that it had been *his* name that the Queen had called out repeatedly as death approached; but giving out that "Bertie" had been Her Majesty's last spoken word doubtlessly provided a more graceful account. Whatever the Queen did or did not say, this was to be the critical moment.

Just after 6.30, Reid and the Kaiser released their arms. The last bulletin of Queen Victoria's reign, this time an unusually straightforward one, was swiftly composed and released to the public: "Her Majesty the Queen breathed Her last at 6.30 p.m., surrounded by Her Children and Grandchildren." After all of the bulletins issued over the preceding days by the Queen's medical team that had been worded in cautious, deceptively embellished prose, the final announcement of her death conveyed a sense of resignation and simplicity.

The death scene: 22–25 January. *"Looking beautiful, surrounded by loose flowers and palms strewn on the bed."*

That evening, Reid assisted the maids and nurse in lifting the Queen's body off of the wheeled utility cot on which she had been placed several days before to provide greater access to her physicians and attendants, now placing it back upon the larger double bed on which she customarily had slept. That was the time that Reid first inspected the woefully emaciated body of Queen Victoria. He observed with surprise that the Queen had a ventral hernia and a prolapse of the uterus. He ought not to have been surprised, however, since the hernia and prolapse were conditions, as Michaela Reid rightly noted, "not uncommon …for a woman who had borne nine children." But Reid had always before seen the Queen fully clothed, seated upright and receiving him with considerable formality; and Sir James himself had remained standing during these audiences. The various potions and "draughts" he had prepared for her when she called at night unable to sleep, had all been administered by her maids.

A few hours after the Queen's death, Reid found that her body, after having been dressed and adorned by her maids, was "looking beautiful, surrounded by loose flowers and palms strewn on the bed." Responsible for the Queen's person in death as he had been in life, Reid himself was not to rest completely until the body was embalmed and the coffin's lid finally sealed fast on 25 January.

One of Sir James's many obligations between the 22nd and 25th of January had been to prepare an official summary of the medical events leading to the death of Queen Victoria. His "Medical Report on the Queen's Death," issued from Osborne on 23 January 1901, cited the weakening effects of a 12-month period of "dyspepsia," poor nutrition, weight loss, and insomnia. By November and December, he wrote, there were also "… occasional slight and transitory attacks of aphasia, the latter indicating that the cerebral circulation had become damaged.…" These aphasic episodes were described as "always of an ephemeral kind and unattended by any motor paralysis."

Sir James's account was for the most part factually correct, but he subtly slanted the text to imply that the Queen's neurological changes had been milder and more recent than they actually were. For example, although he acknowledged that the Queen experienced unusual fatigue after traveling to Osborne on 18 December, he added that she had then seemed to rally until her last days. It was not until 17 January, according to Reid's official statement, that the Queen "showed for the first time unequivocal symptoms of confusion," and also a "slight flattening" of the right side of the face. Emphasis would have to be placed on the word "unequivocal," since Reid had observed marked personality changes, apathy and confusional episodes appearing at least four days prior, on 13 January, and his personal notes further suggest that these developments had a much earlier and more insidious onset.

In his official summary released to the public, Reid seemed to have been striving to preserve the prestige of the monarchy; this was, after all, the institution he had attempted to uphold for 20 years through his efforts to protect the health and buoy the spirits of Queen Victoria. To this end, Sir James' *post-hoc* pronouncements may have been intended to minimize any suggestion of affective mental illness or dementia, two socially stigmatizing conditions. Instead, Reid cited, using intentionally ambiguous phrasing, the effects of "Royal responsibilities and the Imperial events, domestic sorrows and anxieties which have crowded into her life of later years." Even *The Lancet*, the esteemed official medical journal of the British Medical Association, in its 26 January medical report on the Queen's death, euphemistically listed as secondary causes of death after primary cerebral failure, "private griefs and public anxieties" (*The Lancet,* 26 January 1901). This rings very much like Sir James Reid's phrasing, and it is thought that he wrote or contributed significantly to *The Lancet* article.

However, neither "private griefs nor public anxieties" would, even then, have been realistically considered to be *bona fide* causes of death, nor would "overwork," which was cited by an important newspaper obituary (*The Times of London,* 23 January 1901). Reid himself was probably somewhat defensive about how his medical management would be perceived, anticipating the criticism that he ought to have alerted the government to the need for a Regency weeks before the Queen's death. It would not do for the nation and Empire to realize that its head of state had been incapacitated for weeks before her death. So Sir James concluded his own official summary with the following paragraph:

> Beyond the slight right facial flattening there was never any motor paralysis and except for occasional lapses mentioned, the mind cannot be said to have been clouded. Within a few minutes of death The Queen recognized the several Members of her family.

Understandably, but still worthy of mention, there is no mention of depression in any of the official and semi-official medical accounts of Queen Victoria's death.

A thoroughly disoriented British public, most of whom had never known another monarch, were to read the following worshipful words in the *Times of London* on 23 January: "All day long the Angel of Death had been hovering over Osborne House. One could almost hear the beating of his wings, but at half-past 6 those wings were folded, and the Queen was at rest."

By the end of January, Reid himself was finally able to feel and reflect upon his grief. On 2 February, the day after he joined the Royal family as they transported the Queen's coffin from the Isle of Wight to the mainland, he wrote to Susan with characteristic understatement: "My last journey with Bipps is over, and I feel rather sad."

References

Abrams, R.C. (2015). Sir James Reid and the death of Queen Victoria: An early model for end of life care. *The Gerontologist*, *55*, 6, 943–950. https://doi.org/10.1093/geron/gnu016

Editor. (1901). Queen Victoria: Life and reign. *The Times of London*, 23 January, 1901.

Editor. (1901). The death of the Queen. *The Lancet*, *157*, 276–278.

Reid, M. (1987). *Ask Sir James: The life of Sir James Reid, personal physician to Queen Victoria*. Eland Books: London, UK, pp. 200–213.

Packard, J.M. (1998). *Victoria's daughters*. St. Martin's Griffin: New York, NY, p. 263.

Strachey, L. (1921). *Queen Victoria*. Harcourt Brace Jovanovich/First Harvest HB edition. (1978): New York, NY and London, UK, pp. 423–424.

7. The Clinical Science of Queen Victoria's Two Depressions

The first depression

A critical distinction should be made between Queen Victoria's late-life depression and her earlier protracted bereavement for Prince Albert. (The Queen had largely recovered from her grief by the 1880s, but would almost certainly have disagreed with any characterization that implied an easing of her sorrow for her husband, even though the evidence for her recovery is abundant and convincing).

In a frequently-cited 1987 paper in the *Canadian Journal of Psychiatry*, Powles and Alexander applied the then-current psychiatric diagnostic nosology (DSM-III, 1987) to the Queen's mental state in the years immediately following Prince Albert's death. These authors found her to be, at most, dysthymic, or suffering from a chronic low-grade mood disorder, but not from major depression.

A more current view is that Queen Victoria's prolonged grief for Prince Albert is better understood as a particularly intense variant of normal bereavement, accentuated by her dramatic personal style and sanctioned by the reluctance of those around her to object or interfere. Based on the most recent psychiatric nosology (DSM 5, 2013), Queen Victoria for two decades following the death of Prince Albert suffered from *Persistent*

Complex Bereavement Disorder, an entity involving the prolongation, for a period of one year or more, of the acute phase of grief (the stage of longing for and preoccupation with the person who has died). During that two-decade period it is likely that the Queen also met diagnostic criteria for major depression from time to time.

In whatever way her bereavement is characterized, the Queen's long-delayed recovery from Prince Albert's death was in fact more complete than has been widely appreciated by historians. But then, in the summer of 1900, a full major depressive episode took hold and thereafter continued uninterrupted until her death in January, 1901. Apart from her enduring eccentricities, the depression experienced by Queen Victoria during approximately the last five months of her life must be appreciated as a *distinct new entity.*

The second depression

For Queen Victoria, the *ex-post-facto* diagnosis of late-life depression is predicated on the absence of any other medical etiology for her insomnia and anorexia, both of which appeared in the early fall of 1900 and continued until her death five months later. Severe insomnia and loss of appetite are in fact the Queen's principal somatic complaints in the final volume of her Journal, and she discusses them repeatedly and at length.

However, as has been noted earlier, Sir James Reid, her principal physician, had never been granted an opportunity to physically examine the Queen until after her death. Given the limited access Sir James and the Queen's other physicians had to her actual person, the absence of some other underlying cause that might explain her insomnia, anorexia, and progressive weakness (for example, pancreatic or gastric carcinoma, or severe hypothyroidism) can neither be confirmed nor disproven. Yet depression is the only plausible explanation for which there is documentary evidence.

Symptomatically, late-life depression is known to be strongly linked to the twin maladies experienced by Queen Victoria during the last five months of her life, namely, insomnia and anorexia. For Queen Victoria, both symptoms appeared more or less simultaneously in the late summer of 1900, and persisted until her death, whereas the cognitive and cerebrovascular signs did not become apparent until later in the fall.

In common with some older depressed individuals, Queen Victoria rarely complained of depressed mood. When she did, she linked her dysphoria to one or another external factors, not to depression itself. For example, she writes in her Journal on 23 December, 1900: "I felt melancholy as I see so badly" (Victoria, R.I., 1900, pp. 126–127). Instead, she became fearful and also increasingly hypochondriacal—preoccupied with real and imagined ailments. While he was not allowed to examine the Queen physically, Sir James Reid did have numerous opportunities to observe Her Majesty closely, especially during the last year of her life. He was sent for urgently many times during the nights by the Queen, whom he found to be anxious and fearful, but otherwise suffering from nothing more medically acute than gas, constipation, or pain from ill-fitting dentures.

This late-life depressive picture was of course on a different plane entirely from the variant of the term "depression" Queen Victoria famously used on 18 December 1899 in a defiant response to military reversals in South Africa: "Please understand that there is no one depressed in *this* house; we are not interested in the possibilities of defeat; they do not exist."

Personality features and the Queen's depressions

Clinical research has suggested that personality characteristics may be altered in late-life depression; unhappily, however, it is often one's least adaptive, least attractive, traits that are amplified and exaggerated (Abrams, Spielman, Alexopoulos & Klausner, 1998). For Queen Victoria, selfishness and self-pity were frequently evident. Her compassion tended to be infused with more than a touch of grandiosity and was rarely without allusions to herself or to her own losses.

Her Majesty is self-referential even as she considers to the sadness of her newly-widowed eldest child, Victoria, the Empress Frederick. In 1888, on the death of her son-in-law, the Emperor Frederick III of Germany, after a reign of only 99 days, the Queen wrote: "My poor dear Vicky. God help her! ...None of my own sons could be a greater loss. He was so good, so wise, *and so fond of me!*" [emphasis added] (Arnstein, 2003, p. 177). Then, in a letter to Vicky on 12 January 1899 (Ramm, 1990, p. 223) Queen Victoria writes: "It is my greatest pleasure and happiness to be of any use to you, my darling, and to help and comfort others is the one object in life, *when one has gone through so much sorrow as I....*" [emphasis added].

Earlier in her reign, only a few years after Albert's death, she had written to the widowed Mary Todd Lincoln as a kind of state ambassador of grief, demonstrating the same idiosyncratic mix of sympathy, modesty and hubris (Arnstein, 2003, p. 122):

Dear Madam,

Though a stranger to you, I cannot remain silent when so terrible a calamity has fallen upon you and your country, and must express personally my deep and heartfelt sympathy with you under the shocking circumstances of your present dreadful misfortune. No one can better appreciate than I can, who am myself utterly broken hearted by the loss of my own beloved husband, who was the light of my life, my stay, my all....

In the same melodramatic, self-pitying vein, when persuaded to open Parliament in February 1866 (Arnstein, 2003, p. 126), the Queen deemed the public to be extremely "unreasonable and unfeeling...as to long to witness the spectacle of a poor, broken-hearted widow, nervous and shrinking, dragged in deep mourning, ALONE in STATE as a Show, where she used to go supported by her husband...."

Despite her preoccupation with her own losses and the frequently-applied conviction that ordinary rules of conduct did not apply to her as Sovereign, Queen Victoria was able to reach out intermittently with empathy to family and Royal Household members; this quality often secured their lasting affection for her.

But it is her overwhelming feeling of helplessness against the tide of losses that makes the greatest impression on the reader of the final volume of Queen Victoria's Journal (Abrams, 2010). Even presuming that the Journal was substantially refashioned by Princess Beatrice into a document that emphasizes her more sympathetic, sorrowful nature over the narcissistic aspects of her personality, one cannot fail to be moved by the aging Queen's vulnerability to the accumulation of adverse events occurring in the second half of her last year of life.

Here the Queen Empress, a potent character in a symbolic yet pivotal position, experienced several kinds of helplessness: helplessness in reaction to painful losses, and another kind of helplessness, that arising from the depression itself. The latter, the helplessness of depression, entailed a narrowing of her concerns to focus on the self to an even greater extent than previously, an emphasis that survived Princess Beatrice's redactions and can be appreciated in many of her entries in the Journal's last volume. The Queen's increasing hypochondriasis put enormous pressure on her principal physician, Sir James Reid, as it was solely upon Reid that the Queen leaned for support and consolation in her last days and hours.

The vascular model of late-life depression

Late-life depression, whether a first episode in old age or a late recurrence of an earlier condition, entails a greater association with brain changes than depression occurring in younger adulthood. Late-life depression often follows a stroke or other acute medical event. Otherwise, it could ensue from a slower unfolding of cerebrovascular disease related to hypertension or atrial fibrillation. In either of these courses, acute or progressive, late-life depression may proceed eventually to a dénouement of dementia.

While there is little evidence, anywhere in the final volume of her Journal, for Queen Victoria having had significant memory loss, it almost certainly occurred, an open but sparsely recorded secret among courtiers. The Queen had in all likelihood been experiencing cerebrovascular changes over a period of years, those changes consisting of an accumulation of small cortical lesions that eventually became apparent, in turn contributing to the development of her late-life depression.

To summarize thus far: The historical record suggests that Queen Victoria experienced two distinct depressions in her lifetime, the first occurring during the years following the death of Prince Albert (approximately 1861–1881), and the second, her final depression, during the last five months of her life (1900–1901). Between these two depressions there was a nearly two-decade-long period of remission, a "normothymic interregnum," during which time the Queen's stable health and spirits coincided happily with the apogee of Empire.

The first depression was a chronic, characterologically-driven prolongation of mourning consistent with the DSM-5 (2013) designation of *Prolonged Complex Bereavement Disorder,* a condition that, as previously described, requires an extension of the acute phase of mourning beyond 12 months. *Prolonged Complex Bereavement Disorder* is sometimes viewed as interchangeable with the unofficial entity of *"complicated grief,"* but the latter more often suggests a special relationship with the deceased, or a traumatic or unexpected death, while *Prolonged Complex Bereavement Disorder* has neither implication.

The second depression can be characterized in multiple ways, but based on the most recent views of late-life depression, it was most likely an episode of vascular depression that contributed to Her Majesty's death via the combined effects of anorexia, weakness and inanition.

The Queen was largely free from depression during the period of her remission, but at the same time there may have been a clinically silent prodrome attributable to an accumulation of cerebrovascular changes and personal losses. Persons who have had a significant depressive episode in young or mid-adulthood and who therefore have an established vulnerability to depression, are more likely to develop new and severe depressions in old age when they have *also* experienced cerebrovascular insults and personal losses in the years after their initial depression. The cerebrovascular insults lead to inflammatory processes that compromise both the function of the reward and control systems of the brain as well as the mechanisms that permit flexibility and speed in information-processing (Abrams & Alexopoulos, 2018; Taylor, Aizenstein, & Alexopoulos, 2013; van Agtmaal, Houben, Pouwer, Stehouwer, & Schram, 2017).

An alternative way to understand these phenomena would be to consider that older persons with a history of depression earlier in life might have a lower threshold of cerebrovascular events or require fewer or less impactful personal losses to generate a recurrence of depression in old age. Also, the intense emotional experiences of loss and of depression could themselves have neurological repercussions that could contribute to the apathy often seen in older persons with depression.

Consequently, the descriptive term "vascular depression" refers to the final stage of a clinical *sequence*, starting with depression in early or mid-adulthood followed by the development of cerebrovascular disease; manifestations of cerebrovascular disease may not necessarily be identifiable early on but eventually become apparent with TIAs (transient ischemic attacks), strokes, aphasia and other clinical signs and symptoms. (The presence of aphasia suggests that TIAs have occurred in the general area of the left fronto-temporo-parietal region of the brain). The sequence is then concluded by a severe late-life depression.

A likely scenario is that, during her decades of recovery from bereavement, a hypertensive Queen Victoria developed silent infarcts, decreased cerebral perfusion and inflammatory changes that combined to increase her vulnerability to depression at the end of her life. In support of this view is the suggestion that during her final months of life in the late fall and winter of 1900–1901, the Queen began to have memory impairment, aphasic episodes and other symptoms of cognitive impairment. Also, "hard" evidence for hypertensive vascular disease had been uncovered in a deathbed retinal exam by the Queen's German ophthalmologist Professor Pegenstecher; and, during her last days, the Queen was observed by Dr. Reid to have asymmetric facial drooping, evidence that she had a stroke in the internal capsule of the brain.

References

Abrams, R.C. (2010). Late-life depression and the death of Queen Victoria. *International Journal of Geriatric Psychiatry*, *25*(12), 1222–1229. https://doi:10.1002/gps2647.

Abrams, R.C., & Alexopoulos, G.S. (2018). Vascular depression and the death of Queen Victoria. *International Journal of Geriatric Psychiatry*, *33*(12), 1556–1561. https://doi.org/10.1002/gps.4984

Abrams, R.C., Spielman, L., Alexopoulos, G.S., & Klausner, E. (1998). Personality disorder symptoms in elderly depressed patients. *American Journal of Geriatric Psychiatry*, *6*(1), 24–30.

American Psychiatric Association. (1980). *Diagnostic and statistical manual of mental disorders* (third edition). American Psychiatric Publishing, Inc.: Washington, D.C.

American Psychiatric Association. (2013). *Diagnostic and statistical manual of mental disorders* (fifth edition). American Psychiatric Publishing, Inc.: Arlington, VA.

Arnstein, W.L. (2003). *Queen Victoria*. Palgrave Macmillan: New York, NY, pp. 122, 126, 177.

Hibbert, C. (2000). *Queen Victoria: A personal history*. Da Capo Press: Cambridge, MA, p. 163.

Powles, W.E., & Alexander, M.G. (1987). Was Queen Victoria depressed? 1. Natural history and differential diagnosis of presenting problem. *Canadian Journal of Psychiatry*, *32*(1), 14–19.

Ramm, A. (Ed.). (1990). *Beloved & darling child: Last letters between Queen Victoria & her eldest daughter, 1896–1901*. Sutton Publishing, Stroud, UK, pp. 221, 223.

Taylor, W.D., Aizenstein, H.J., & Alexopoulos, G.S. (2013). The vascular depression hypothesis: Mechanisms linking vascular disease with depression. *Molecular Psychiatry, 18*(9), 963–974. https://doi.10.1038/mp.2013.20

van Agtmaal, M.J.M., Houben, A.J.H.M., Pouwer, F., Stehouwer, C.D.A., & Schram, M.T. (2017). Association of microvascular dysfunction with late-life depression: A systematic review and meta-analysis. *Journal of the American Medical Association Psychiatry, 74*(7):729–739. https://doi.10.1001/jamapsychiatry.2017.0984

Victoria, R.I. (1900). *Queen Victoria's Journal (Royal Archives), 23 December, 1900,* pp. 126–127.

8. Between Two Depressions: A Portrait of Queen Victoria at the Pinnacle

The Queen's recovery from bereavement for Prince Albert

At the 1887 Golden Jubilee marking the 50th year since her accession, Queen Victoria in superficial appearances remained the perpetually grieving widow: She continued for the rest of her life to be steeped in the trappings of mourning, wearing dresses of somber black bombazine, topped by her wedding veil for portraits or otherwise a widow's cap. She had enshrined the Prince Consort's rooms at Windsor and insisted on preserving them exactly as they had been on the day he died in 1861.

But in other ways, by the time of the 1887 Jubilee, Queen Victoria seemed in a deeper sense to at last have recovered from her grief over Prince Albert's death twenty-six years earlier, even if she never fully acknowledged that fact. She had also largely emerged from mourning for other family members, friends and servants. Although she had never been and would never be, even at her happiest interludes, light-heartedly joyful, it is fair to say that by the mid–1880s the Queen's self-pitying ruminations had become less frequent and less severe, and she was more emotionally stable than she had been in the first two decades of her widowhood.

Earlier, her protracted mourning impressed nearly all as excessive, even for her time, class and place, and it had caused her family to fear for the future of the monarchy. But the Queen's behavior had been reinforced by the unquestioningly supportive, if not sycophantic, milieu of the Court.

Queen Victoria had often raged against those who did not share her conservative, expansionist politics, such as her nemesis and four-time Prime Minister, William Gladstone, but by the 1880s the histrionic aspects of her reactions had moderated along with the intensity of grieving. Even if she continued to mourn Albert, the melancholic aspect had receded.

Neither philistine nor anhedonic, the Queen enjoyed travel, music, theatre, food, even whiskey. During the last decade of her life she ventured abroad on regular vacations in the spring. Starting in 1890, she journeyed most years to the south of France or Italy, to Biarritz, Aix-les-Bains, Grasse, Hyeres, and Florence. From 1895 until 1899, she chose Cimiez, near Nice, each time; her last two visits there were to the new Hotel Excelsior, renamed the Excelsior Regina in her honor. How much she actually saw of these lovely havens or imbibed of their atmosphere and spirit is open to question, as she essentially recreated in each place the aura of her own homes on foreign soil.

The Queen brought with her on holidays abroad a large number of her Household members, altogether an enormous suite that included personal maids and other servants, and sometimes her doctor. She also took her own bed and her donkey. In *Queen Mary*, Pope-Hennessy (1959, p. 344) reported that for these logistically complex travels, "every detail of the installation of the Court was carefully supervised, and even the writing-paper was identical...with that of Windsor Castle or Balmoral, the only difference being the words, 'Hotel Regina, Cimiez,' beneath the embossed crown." When she did tour pleasing or important sites, she would sometimes hold up a miniature of Albert, or even speak to it, as if to share with him by sight or verbal description the experiences he was missing (Weintraub, 1988).

But whatever she saw or failed to see, there is no doubt that the Queen had sufficiently recovered from her mourning to enjoy herself on these eccentric sojourns and felt them to have invigorating effects which lingered on after she returned home. In a letter dated 28 April 1888, Marie Mallet (Mallet, 1968, p. 17) described the Queen on her return from continental travels: "The Queen [was]…looking as fresh as a daisy. …Her Majesty was most cheerful at dinner and has fully enjoyed her trip abroad. She talked and laughed incessantly.…"

Enjoyment of music and the arts

The Queen's appreciation of music and theatre was always on an emotional level. A demonstratively enthusiastic but not always discerning critic, she judged the quality of performances mainly by their power to move her. For her 80th birthday at Windsor, there was a performance of excerpts from *Lohengrin,* and the Queen, quoted or paraphrased by Lady Lytton (Lutyens, 1962, p. 140), declared herself

> 'simply enchanted. It is the most glorious composition, so poetic, so dramatic, and one might almost say, religious in feeling and full of sadness, pathos and tenderness. The singing of the two brothers [Jean and Edouard de Reszke] was beyond praise…. The whole opera produced a great impression on me.'

Queen Victoria's personal and emotional response to music sometimes distracted her from a critical appraisal of the quality of compositions and performances. As Marie Mallet wrote in 1889 (Mallet, 1968, p. 31): "… The Queen is rather fond of second-rate pieces….," provided they offered an emotional lift. However, Marie had appeared to upgrade her view of the Queen's taste in music by 1897, when she described Her Majesty's reaction to a concert at Windsor (Mallet, 1968, p. 121):

We had some lovely music this evening at St. George's Hall. Sir Arthur Sullivan came to conduct an Anthem he has written at the Queen's request for December 14th [anniversary of the Prince Consort's death], and the choir from St. George's conducted by him sang it most beautifully, as well as several other things, *Peace, Come Away*, by Stanford and a piece by Loebgesang. The Queen enjoyed it all to the full, I have never seen anyone more worthy of music and moved by it than she is.

The years from approximately 1895 through 1899 defined the period when the Queen was optimally recovered from mourning for Prince Albert and for her son-in-law Prince Henry of Battenberg (Liko), but had not yet lost her son Prince Alfred (Affie), nor her grandson Prince Christian Victor of Schleswig-Holstein (Christle). This interval, climaxed by the 1897 Jubilee celebrations, was for the Queen a "golden age" between her two principal periods of depression. During this time Lady Lytton recorded the Queen's reactions to various private performances which were held for the Court at Osborne, Balmoral or Windsor. These reactions were not those of a depressed woman.

After one such occasion at Balmoral in 1895, Lady Lytton (Lutyens, 1962, p. 43) wrote:

We had many artists quietly in the dining-room after dinner, Wolff, Albani, Hollman, Clara Butt, Salmond and Pugno.... I sat by the Queen and her manner to the radiant artists was perfect, and they were so happy and each did extra well. ...The household supped with the artists and guests and it was very merry.

On 6 December 1897 Queen Victoria wrote to her eldest daughter the Empress Frederick in Berlin (Ramm, 1990, p. 209): "We are going to hear Grieg and his wife play and sing his beautiful composition this evening. Some three weeks ago we heard Mde Chaminde play her charming compositions which she did beautifully...." As late as January 1899, at Osborne, Lady Lytton wrote (Lutyens, 1962, p. 138):

> Monday, 16th and Wednesday, 18th there were very nice concerts in the Durbar Room. Clara Butt sang well...and Herr Wolff (violin) at the second. It was nice to see the Queen at a party and she enjoyed it and was so keen and it was quite a treat for us all....

The Queen was broad-minded enough to have invited the actress Sarah Bernhardt to perform for her in 1893, even though her own, more conventional daughter, the Empress Frederick, branded Bernhardt as "immoral." (Lutyens, 1962, p. 104). There is no documentation of the Queen's reaction, but the actress' "awful reputation" was well known in advance, and one presumes the performance was enjoyed anyway by both the Monarch and her Court.

Return of the Queen's appetite

Until the onset of her final depression in the fall of 1900, when she suddenly began to experience severe anorexia, the Queen's appetite had been prodigious, and she had gained weight steadily. On 3 November 1888 Marie Mallet highlights Victoria's hearty appetite and, despite a general shyness and reticence, her lack of inhibition in describing her pleasure (Mallet, 1968, p. 23): "...I dined with the Queen last night and beheld her peel and eat a

Ledbury apple with evident relish and many expressions of admiration as to size, beauty and flavour...."

Similarly, on a "cheerful" October afternoon at Balmoral in 1897, Lady Lytton describes the Queen's enjoyment of afternoon tea after a drive (Lutyens, 1962, p. 124): "The Queen had a good appetite and after two scones, two bits of toast and several biscuits she said, 'I am afraid I must not have any more.'" Supporting this impression, the visiting Aga Khan wrote after dining with the Queen: "She had... every course, including both the hot and iced pudding...."

If the Queen was in the habit of "having every course," one must respect the quantity of what she must have consumed at a typical Household luncheon on 25 March 1899 during her spring visit to Cimiez (Mallet, 1968, p. 161):

Household Luncheon

Risotto à la Milanaise
Grilled mutton chops
Poulets aux nouilles
Asperges à la sauce
Tapioca pudding
Meringues aux fraises

In her letter to her family on that date, Marie Mallet wrote: "What do you think of our Menus? I hope you don't imagine we have conversation to match!"

Emotional resilience restored

If, in James Pope-Hennessy's memorable phrase, "high spirits were never the key to the Queen's heart," Her Majesty, within the parameters of her mostly self-imposed perpetual mourning, at last seemed willing to enjoy life again, and she displayed an increasing capacity to do so (Pope-Hennessy, 1959, p. 33). Lady Lytton (Lutyens, 1962, p. 46) cites the Queen's flamboyant granddaughter Queen Marie of Romania (née Princess Marie of Edinburgh and Coburg) as the source of the observation that "'the Queen's rooms, wherever she was, smelt of orange flower even when no flowers were there.'" Then Lady Lytton herself asks dreamily: "Was this smell of orange flower always surrounding the Queen part of her attraction?"

By the late 1880s the Queen began to demonstrate an emotional resilience she had lacked previously, especially in the 1860s, the immediate post-Albert years, and through the 1870s, the nadir of her popularity; this reserve of strength and flexibility did not begin to seriously fail her until the summer of 1900. After the death in South Africa of Princess Beatrice's husband, Liko Battenberg, on 20 January 1896, Her Majesty wrote in her Journal (Victoria, R.I., 1896): "There is such grief in the house…What have we not all lost in beloved, noble Liko…My heart aches for my darling child [Princess Beatrice]…." However, less than one month later, Lady Lytton (Lutyens, 1962, p. 53) describes a conversation with the Queen in which she still laments the loss of Prince Henry:

…but after a time she could talk of other things as well, the coming moves to Nice and Windsor and hoping to see Lord Salisbury soon …and sometimes even the beautiful smile broke across her face in the wonderful way it does.

The presence of Beatrice's and Liko's children, who lived with their mother at Osborne, enlivened the Royal household and cheered its mistress. It was noted by many, with some astonishment, that the Queen indulged the young "Batts" (Battenbergs), allowing them freedom to play loudly and run through the rooms and grounds of Osborne. She had never permitted her own children these liberties, but the presence of a new generation in her house without doubt helped Queen Victoria to weather the stunning loss of Prince Henry.

By July of 1899 the Queen was still in excellent form and at least outwardly free from depression. At this time Marie Mallet was cheered to find that "The Queen is the picture of health and in excellent spirits" (Mallet, 1968, pp. 171–172). That same summer, on 16 August at Osborne, Lady Lytton (Lutyens, 1962, p. 144) recorded that she "drove with the Queen and she and Princess Christian talked so cheerfully and happily. The sunset was perfectly beautiful with scarlet red green blue sky and grey cloud effects." The death of Affie on 30 July 1900 was to change much of that, but for the moment the Queen carried on contentedly.

Queen Victoria herself wrote to Vicky on 17 October 1890 (Ramm, 1990, pp. 114–115) during her autumn Scottish sojourn, sending the letter directly from Glassalt Shiel, the isolated rustic house which was her distant outpost on the already-remote Balmoral estate. The miserable weather and pain in her legs had done nothing to diminish her buoyant outlook:

> Beatrice and I with Emily Ampthill and Minnie Cochrane* came here yesterday for luncheon in an awful storm of wind and rain…but the dear little house was warm and comfortable and this morning,

---

* Minnie (Minna) Cochrane, daughter of Adm. Sir Thomas John Cochrane, was a member of the family that owned Quarr Abbey, a house five miles from Osborne on the Isle of Wight. It was at Quarr Abbey that Princess Beatrice spent her honeymoon after marrying Prince Henry of Battenberg in 1885. Minnie Cochrane later became a lady-in-waiting to Princess Beatrice.

though slight showers may still come on, is bright with little wind. We return after luncheon; for I have my masseuse for my legs, an excellent woman, at Balmoral and ought not to lose more than a day. But my legs are better and imagine! I danced quadrilles the night before last and twice before! We had a beautiful small band of eight who play with an *entrain* like Strauss and render all sorts of things... nice quiet people who really play quite delightfully...

Queen Victoria loved no place more than Balmoral and cherished all things Scottish, including the dark, biting weather often encountered in the Highlands, even in the early autumn. Sir James Clark, one of Sir James Reid's predecessors as Physician-in-Ordinary, had years earlier planted the notion in the mind of the suggestible Queen that colder temperatures were healthful, and balmy ones the opposite, a simplistic and dubious prescription to which she adhered faithfully until her final depression in the fall of 1900, when she suddenly became intolerant of cold. Accordingly, she rarely permitted fires at the Castle. Lady Lytton records: "There was usually a Minister in Attendance at Balmoral, but it was so dull and cold there that the Ministers dreaded having to go." Lord James of Hereford, for example, once described the Castle as "cold as death" (Lutyens, 1962, p. 16).

But the Queen was at her happiest in the Highlands. During a visit to Balmoral in the late summer of 1896, the Tsar of Russia, husband of her granddaughter Princess Alix of Hesse, wrote to his mother that "Granny was kinder and more amiable than ever" (Lutyens, 1962, p. 165). In 1895, Lady Lytton famously captured Queen Victoria at Balmoral speaking with a Scottish inflection; referring to a pensioner on the estate, Her Majesty is reported to have said: "I always give her five poond" (Lutyens, 1962, p. 36).

Although she never gave up her black dresses, by the mid-1890s these somber frocks were on special occasions enlivened with jewelry, and her bonnets were more frequently trimmed with flowers. She was persuaded, at least once in her long widowhood, reputedly by the Princess of Wales, to depart from wearing unrelieved black. The occasion was the banquet at Buckingham Palace on the evening before the great Jubilee procession in 1897, to which she wore a dress embroidered with gold, a diamond necklace and diamonds in her cap (HH Princess Marie Louise, 1956, p. 146).

But the Queen did not always like black when worn by others, particularly clergy. Princess Marie Louise (HH Princess Marie Louise, 1956, p. 146) describes an occasion in 1897, when the Queen had received a hundred Bishops attending a conference:

> Her Majesty was at Windsor, and had had an exhausting reception.... When it was all over she went for her usual afternoon drive. Edith, Lady Lytton, was in waiting and accompanied her. There was rather a prolonged silence at first, and then the Queen said 'A very ugly party.' Of course, black shovel hats, black gaiters, black silk aprons, and the whole rather gloomy tailoring of these worthy prelates was a striking contrast to the gorgeous and colourful Indian and Eastern guests she had been entertaining for the occasion of the Diamond Jubilee held that year. Then after a further pause, 'I do not like bishops.' Edith Lytton nearly fell out of the carriage in surprise and horror. 'Oh, but your dear Majesty likes *some* bishops....' 'Yes,' said her gracious Majesty, 'I like the man but *not* the bishop!'

So Queen Victoria may have been the titular head of the Church of England, but clerical politics and religious doctrine, beyond her core faith in an afterlife featuring a rapturous reunion with Albert, had never been her preoccupations. Her precocious young great-grandson, Prince Edward of York (eventually King Edward VIII and ultimately Duke of Windsor) is reported to have observed that the Queen, whom he called "Gangan," would not enjoy being in Heaven, because there she would be preceded by the Angels (Bryan & Murphy, 1979, p. 55).

The Queen seemed to retain sufficient energy before the fall of 1900 to write numerous and substantial letters to her children, especially to the Empress Frederick in Germany, and to those grandchildren who were particularly favored or who were experiencing personal setbacks at the time. She especially enjoyed the role of confidante to her young single granddaughters, and if these exchanges were in person, the Queen-Empress would assume an unintimidating, confessional manner, almost girlish, her facial expression likened to that of "an amiable field mouse" (Pope-Hennessy, 1959, p. 205).

At the same time she looked upon her role as the head of state with the utmost gravity; she remained informed of all important policy matters, studied their minutiae, and tirelessly pressed her domestically conservative and internationally expansionist points of view on her Prime Ministers. The four-time Prime Minister in her reign, William Gladstone, with whom the Queen maintained a strong mutual dislike, found her exacting and exhausting: "…enough to kill a man." (Weintraub, 1988, p. 448).

New relationships with men

Queen Victoria, fatherless from infancy after the early death of the Duke of Kent from pneumonia, and restricted to a women's world throughout her childhood and later as a widowed female Sovereign, loved men and the company of men all her life. This fact goes far toward explaining her sustained attraction to several male servants, notably the Scottish ghillie John Brown, and after Brown's death, Abdul Karim (the "Munshi," or teacher, whom she promoted from the status of servant to a more dignified role as her personal tutor for Urdu).

Several prominent biographers (Hibbert, 2000; Weintraub, 1988) have thought that the Queen had been, knowingly or not, attracted to Lord Melbourne, the first Prime Minister of her reign and something of an avuncular figure when she was herself still a teenager. Next, of course, was Albert himself, in her mind an uncrowned king. Although she never felt that any other man approached Albert's overwhelming masculine beauty (a view not widely shared by others), she often commented in her Journal and in letters on male attractiveness. As one of many examples, in a letter to the Empress Frederick dated 6 December 1891, she wrote: "Tonight we have Prince Napoleon here [son of her friends the Emperor and Empress].... He is very good-looking with a fine presence and pleasing" (Ramm, 1990, p. 136).

For years after the death of her personal servant, Prince Albert's former Scottish ghillie, John Brown, Queen Victoria memorialized him in a manner that seemed excessive, embarrassing and even infuriating to her children, who themselves had rarely received such signs of respect or tenderness from her. She next turned for solace to Sir James Reid and other medical men, and also to her son-in-law Liko Battenberg, all of whom had reassuring masculine energy. When Liko died in 1896, she clung even closer to Reid—whose late marriage to the Hon. Susan Baring she accepted only grudgingly—and to Abdul Karim, the Munshi. As a servant, Abdul had been universally despised by members of the Queen's Household as fraudulently jumped-up from lower-class origins and also an inveterate mischief-maker; the Queen nevertheless was strongly drawn to him and elevated him partly to protect him from the hostility of her Household and to soothe his wounded feelings.

Queen Victoria herself readily acknowledged what was apparent to all, her need of male companionship. In her letter to the Empress Frederick of 3 January 1897 the Queen refers to the emptiness she felt after Liko's death, an emotion she experienced "severely":

I have just taken leave of Arthur and Louischen. It is such a comfort and help to have him in the house. The loss of a male relative is severely felt. Dear Liko was such a help. (Ramm, 1990, p. 198).

Curiously, she closes this letter, containing as it does a revealing self-observation, with the line: "I must end this stupid letter to save the messenger," as if by self-denigration to disavow or dilute the truth of what she has just written.

Victorian social prejudices were never for Victoria herself. The woman in whose name class boundaries and social strictures were rigidly promulgated enforced them irregularly for her own purposes, and tended to abandon them entirely when they involved a man to whom she was physically attracted or upon whom she was emotionally dependent. Prior to the appointment of James Reid as her principal physician, the Queen's medical staff, regardless of position within their own hierarchy, did not dine officially with the Royal Household; socially they inhabited a nebulous position midway between Royal servants and the aristocratic members of the Queen's Household. However, in addition to the respect he earned for the tactful but honest manner in which he carried out his professional responsibilities, Reid was popular with all and considered to be a warm and amusing presence in a Court that otherwise took on a decidedly gloomy tone. Then Dr. Reid took to entertaining those members of the Household who did not happen to be dining with the Queen on a given day. The Queen heard of these gatherings that were greatly enjoyed by those who attended, and felt quite removed from the fun. "I hear Dr. Reid gives dinner parties," she said wistfully one day. Soon thereafter, a social barrier was breached, and Reid began to dine with the Household on a regular basis. Eventually, as his standing advanced further, he was promoted to a Baronetcy and married a Household member, the Hon. Susan Baring. The Queen's initial outraged rant objecting to the

Reid–Baring marriage was not based on the social disparities between the couple, but was more evidently a reaction of jealousy, or of concern that she would lose the full attention of her devoted physician and friend (Reid, 1987).

A great old age: When Queen Victoria was at her best

There is evidence from many sources that in old age Queen Victoria had at last recovered from Albert's death, but there were still times when she would reprise her long-sorrowing widow persona, as on the anniversary of the Prince Consort's death (Pope-Hennessy, 1959). To some, the Queen appeared to use what remained of her grief to do what she wanted and evade what she did not (Weintraub, 1988). Her private secretary, the harried and sometimes archly sarcastic Sir Henry Ponsonby, hearing that the Queen had refused to host the traditional Sovereign's Drawing Room in 1892, wrote: "Princess B seems to think it possible that H.M. wd go to one Drawing Room. But H.M. in sad and mournful tones said to me she was damned if she would" (Ponsonby, 1944, p. 64). Yet her subjects' eagerness to forgive the Queen her years of withdrawal, and her own increasing willingness to appear publicly as Sovereign, were to come together in her final years as a time of "apotheosis" (Strachey, 1921, p. 406).

For the most part, Queen Victoria in her last years had fully embraced her role, even with its declining prerogatives. She was a passionate, unyielding Conservative. She adored Benjamin Disraeli, who "made" her Emperor of India by pushing a bill through Parliament, but unreservedly despised William Gladstone, a person she believed would never defend the Empire and who, even worse, she felt contributed to the discontent of the working classes, thereby undermining the political supremacy of the aristocracy. She was partisan to the point, at times, of being constitutionally indiscreet. But she was also deeply knowledgeable and steeped in world affairs and politics. That, aside from presiding over the mechanics of government and making public appearances, was in fact all that remained of her official role. Her remaining trio of constitutional rights, memorably elucidated by the scholar Walter Bagehot (1955)—to be informed, to advise, and to warn—had become essentially meaningless over the course of Gladstone's four ministries. During those ministries the Queen was less than optimally informed by the Prime Minister, and her advice and warnings went largely unheeded.

Conservative as she was, the Queen was in many ways an independent thinker. She was refreshingly free of prejudices common to her time and class. As Queen Victoria saw it, as the Sovereign of the United Kingdom and Empress of India, her decisions should go unchallenged when it came to such personal matters as the suitability of candidates for marriage to her children and grandchildren. In that area she broke precedent by allowing her fourth daughter, Princess Louise, to marry Lord Lorne, a commoner (albeit one of exalted status and ancient lineage). She scoffed at the German royal courts' snobbish attitude toward the semi-royal offspring of morganatic marriages, for example, the Battenbergs* and the Tecks, whom she warmly welcomed into her immediate family: One Battenberg prince became her son-in-law, while his brother married a Hesse granddaughter. Then, with the Queen's connivance, a seemingly unmarriageable Teck princess discredited by the taint of her paternal morganatic blood, a princess for whom every possible matrimonial match would be automatically deemed a mésalliance,

---

* Queen Victoria allowed her youngest daughter, Princess Beatrice, to marry Prince Henry of Battenberg and her favorite granddaughter, Princess Victoria of Hesse, to marry Prince Louis of Battenberg, a brother of Prince Henry. When members of the German Royal house, including the Queen's own grandsons, voiced disapproval of Prince Henry as a prospective husband for Princess Beatrice on the grounds of his imperfect Royal descent, Queen Victoria indignantly wrote: "…if the Queen of England thinks a person is good enough for her daughter what have other people got to say?" (Weintraub, 1988, p. 470).

was awarded the greatest prizes of all, to be engaged to marry to two direct heirs to the throne, the first being Prince Albert Victor of Wales, and then on his death, his younger brother, Prince George. History has, in the view of many, borne out the foresight of Queen Victoria, when the former Princess May of Teck, as the widowed Queen Mary, took on a crucial stabilizing role for the monarchy during the crisis surrounding the abdication of King Edward VIII in 1936–37. Another area in which Queen Victoria was progressive, surprisingly so considering her reflexive conservativism, was her impatience with racial or ethnic prejudice, whether in the Royal Household or in domestic or international politics.

It is possible to sum up all these observations by simply asserting that in old age Queen Victoria was at her best. Her body was aging, to be sure, but as late as 1 June 1897, Marie Mallet was still able to write: "The Queen is a marvel of health and strength" (Mallet, 1968, p. 108). She had, moreover, recovered from private grief, achieved a mastery of her role, and was now a figure of reverence to many.

Describing Queen Victoria in the fall of 1891, Pope-Hennessy (p. 205) wrote:

> This extremely small old lady of seventy-two, lame in one leg and dressed in stiff black silk, with a soft, white, lace cap upon her white hair, had an imposing dignity about her. She was surrounded by an atmosphere of genuine awe. Thickly carpeted corridors led to her private apartments, which smelled of orange-flower water. Door after door would be noiselessly opened until one reached the inner sanctum and came face to face with this diminutive figure in black.

No less esteemed a figure in medicine than the neurologist William Gowers seemed moved and inspired by the Queen's demeanor when he traveled to Osborne in August 1898 to receive a baronetcy. His brief description shows

Queen Victoria at the cusp of her decline, her charisma still intact but the fatigue apparent:

> The Queen looked careworn but less wrinkled & less old than I expected. Her glance is keen but her voice soft & gentle, as she said, twice, 'Sir William' when she touched first one shoulder & then the other with the flat of an old carved light sword. (Scott, Eadie & Lees, 2012).

References

Bagehot, W. (1955). *The English constitution.* Humphrey Milford; Oxford University Press: Jericho, UK.

Bryan, J., & Murphy, C.J.V. (1979). *The Windsor story.* William Morrow & Company, Inc.: New York, NY, p. 55.

Hibbert, C. (2000). *Queen Victoria: A personal history.* Da Capo Press: Cambridge, MA.

Lutyens, M. (Ed.). (1962). *Lady Lytton's court diary: 1895–1899.* Rupert Hart-Davis: London, UK, pp. 43, 46, 53, 124, 138, 140, 144, 165.

Mallet, V. (Ed.). (1968). *Life with Queen Victoria: Marie Mallet's letters from court, 1887–1901.* Houghton Mifflin Company: Boston, MA, pp. 17, 23, 31, 121.

Ponsonby, A. (Lord Ponsonby of Shulbrede). (1944). *Henry Ponsonby: Queen Victoria's private secretary.* The Macmillan Company: New York, NY, p. 64.

Pope-Hennessy, J. (1959). *Queen Mary.* George Allen & Unwin Limited: London, UK, pp. 33, 205, 316, 344.

HH Princess Marie Louise. (1956). *My memories of six reigns.* Evans Brothers Limited: London, UK, p. 146.

Reid, M. (1987). *Ask Sir James: The life of Sir James Reid, personal physician to Queen Victoria.* Eland Books: London, UK.

Ramm, A. (Ed.). 1990. *Beloved & darling child: Last letters between Queen Victoria & her eldest daughter, 1896–1901.* Sutton Publishing: Stroud, UK, pp. 114–115, 136, 198.

Scott, A. Eadie, M., & Lees, A. (2012). *William Richard Gowers, 1845–1915: Exploring the Victorian brain.* Oxford, UK: Oxford University Press.

Strachey, L. (1921). *Queen Victoria.* Harcourt Brace Jovanovich/First Harvest HB Edition. (1978): New York, NY and London, UK, p. 406.

Victoria, R.I. (1896). *Queen Victoria's Journal (Royal Archives), 20 January, 1896.*

Weintraub, S. (1988). *Victoria: An intimate biography.* Truman Talley Books/ E.P. Dutton: New York, NY, pp. 448, 470, 501, 515.

9.   Victorian Disability and Loss

An aggregation of impairments

Meanwhile, over time, Queen Victoria was acquiring geriatric disabilities, now understood to be strong predictors of major depression in later life. By 1900 the Queen was unable to walk unsupported, having first required the use of a cane, then a rolling chair. This dependence on assistive devices was compounded by increasing weight on her short frame. The inability to walk independently had had a more gradual onset than her other disabilities, but there were many vicissitudes within a conspicuously downward course.

In the spring of 1871, at the age of 52, Queen Victoria had been able to climb the steepest face of Craig Gowan in Scotland. However, shortly after that she injured a knee, missing a step going down a staircase at Windsor. From this accident she slowly recovered, but she would complain of residual knee pain for the rest of her life. As one biographer (Weintraub, 1988) has pointed out, the Queen had in the past temporarily lost her ability to walk during periods of acute grief or stress, hinting at a disability that, if not purely hysterical, was at the least in part emotionally-driven. A state of semi-paralysis or temporary motor incapacitation occurred after Albert's death in 1861; again in 1871, when her unpopularity peaked; and for a longer period than before, nearly a year, after her servant John Brown's death in

1883, when she keenly felt the absence of his strong arm on which to lean, both physically and metaphorically.

In 1890 the Queen was seen in public using a walking stick, but in the latter part of that same year, she was still able to dance quadrilles at Balmoral (Ramm, 1990, p. 114). It was not until the fall of 1891 that she was unequivocally regarded as "lame" by the visiting Princess May of Teck. By 1893, the Empress Frederick wrote that "she has great difficulty in moving and getting about—in getting up from her chair." Reflecting on the unevenness of the aging process, Empress Frederick in the same letter observed, as did others before and after, that the Queen's "...smile & voice & complexion" appeared to be "as young as years ago" (Pope-Hennessey, 1959, p. 286).

Then, by the end of the 1890s, Queen Victoria was unable even to balance her weight on her legs. She attempted to compensate by continuing the ritual of her daily drives, whether at Windsor, Osborne or Balmoral. On these drives she would typically invite a daughter, granddaughter, lady in waiting or visitor to accompany her. Such occasions tended to be tense affairs for the invited lady, who had to consider the content and implications of every response with care, but Queen Victoria herself definitely enjoyed them. The Queen had always taken such outings, finding them invigorating, and famously did so even in damp or bracing weather, which for many years she believed to have health-promoting qualities. Eventually these excursions became invested with a nearly ceremonial importance as the centerpiece of her day. She viewed them as exercise, but she was actually lifted in and out of the carriage, such that no muscular exertion, save for sitting upright, was involved.

The Queen's eyesight had also begun to seriously fail, and she had increasing difficulty reading state documents; but she flatly rejected the use of typewriters, an innovation that might have helped, at least early on.

"These ingenious machines are paralysed by the Queen's displeasure," wrote Lord Rosebery, then Foreign Secretary (Rose, 1984, p. 48).

Meanwhile, Her Majesty's cataracts, on both eyes, grew until she was for practical purposes almost completely blind by the end of her life. The Queen often complains in the last volume of her Journal of the autumnal darkness at Balmoral and Windsor, a phenomenon fairly attributable to some extent to the cloudy weather and the shortening days of the season, and probably not helped by her depressed mood, but certainly compounded by her low vision. She could now crochet only with great difficulty (Lutyens, 1962). More importantly, she was compelled in her last years to have newspapers and official papers read to her.

For reasons of security, the task of reading confidential State documents to Queen Victoria at this point devolved on Princess Beatrice, the blood relative closest to the Queen who was on the scene. As has been described previously, to the consternation of many, Princess Beatrice performed this task perfunctorily. In so doing, she assumed an attitude quite unlike that in her own later years, which she willingly devoted to the enormous task of copying and editing of her mother's Journal.

As late as August 1898, a young Frederick Ponsonby, then one of the Queen's assistant private secretaries, wrote to his mother decrying the lax attitude of Princess Beatrice in reading documents aloud. Here Ponsonby distinguishes the Sovereign's failing vision from her still-intact intellect:

> The sad thing is that it is only her eyes and nothing else. Her memory
> is still wonderful, her shrewdness [sic] her power of discrimination
> as strong as ever [sic] her long experience of European politics alone
> makes her opinion invaluable but when her sole means of reading
> dispatches, *précis*, debates etc. lie in [Princess]B[eatrice], it is simply
> hopeless. (Ponsonby, 1898).

But it was the Queen's dutiful, self-effacing amanuensis, Thora, Princess Christian's daughter Helena Victoria, who took dictation for the majority of Journal entries throughout 1900, the last full year of Queen Victoria's life.

Losses sustained by Queen Victoria

By her final months of life, Queen Victoria had endured numerous losses; for a while she seemed numbed or dazed by their number and importance. By the fall of 1900, the Queen had seen the death of her mother, the Duchess of Kent (1860); her husband Prince Albert (1861); her half-sister Princess Feodora of Leiningen, one of the few companions of her early childhood (1872); her second daughter and third child, Princess Alice, Grand Duchess of Hesse and by Rhine, the victim of a typhus epidemic in Darmstadt (1878); her Prime Minister and friend Benjamin Disraeli (1881); her servant and confidant, John Brown (1883); her fourth son and eighth child, Prince Leopold, the Duke of Albany, a hemophiliac who bled to death after a fall (1884); her much-loved son-in-law Fritz (Emperor Frederick III, husband of Vicky), with whom also died her hopes for a liberal, peace-loving Germany closely allied by familial ties to the British crown (1888); her grandson and the ultimate heir to the throne, Prince Albert Victor of Wales, the Duke of Clarence and Avondale, who died of influenza shortly after his engagement to Princess May of Teck (1892); her longtime Private Secretary, Sir Henry Ponsonby (1895); her beloved son-in-law, Liko (Prince Henry of Battenberg) (1896); her grandson "young Alfred," son and heir to the Duke of Edinburgh and Coburg (1898); and his father, Prince Alfred (Affie), her second son and fourth child (1900). This is only a partial list that does not include many other friends and servants.

But as clearly shown in her Journal entries, the blow Queen Victoria felt most keenly was the death, in Pretoria, on October 29, 1900, of her adored grandson Prince Christian Victor (Christle) of Schleswig-Holstein. With the deaths of Affie and Christle, by the last half-year of her life, Queen Victoria was in a state of continuous mourning, capped by the sudden demise of her devoted friend Lady Churchill at Osborne only weeks before Her Majesty's own death.

That some of these relatives and servants were not as high in the Queen's esteem in life as they had become in death is not considered in the Journal. To cite one example, she had bitterly opposed the marriage of Princess Beatrice to Liko, although that reaction was partly explained by the fact that she could not at the time accept that her youngest daughter would marry at all, and partly by her typical cold-heartedness when the matter concerned her own needs; such cold-heartedness presented a jarring departure from her self-concept as a kind, emotionally generous person. Despite her initial begrudging attitude toward Beatrice's match, the Queen came to love and admire Liko as her son-in-law-in-residence, and she soon relished having his robust, spirited presence in her home. However, in a pattern that suggested her mourning for Albert, it was only after his death that Liko was raised to her personal pantheon of martyred heroes.

It was in 1898, after learning of the assassination of the Empress of Austria, that Queen Victoria at last acknowledged having had a peer in the "aristocracy of suffering," at least in the number and severity of losses and tragedies endured. The Queen had never been inclined to understatement, but in this case the facts spoke for themselves. On 11 September 1898 (Ramm, 1990, p. 221) Her Majesty wrote to the Empress Frederick: "I am dumb with horror at this horrible event. ...What a fatality in her [the Empress's] family. Her cousin drowned, her son murdered or committed suicide, her sister burnt and herself stabbed to death!"

Regarding the Empress Frederick's own health, Queen Victoria was probably not informed in detail of her eldest daughter's diagnosis of metastatic cancer, but Her Majesty was too realistic and generally well informed not to suspect the worst. In an earlier letter to the Empress Frederick after the latter's visit to Osborne over Christmas in 1899, the Queen, alert to the lack of privacy for her personal post and aware that Vicky had few friends in Germany, devised a cagey strategy to maintain secrecy (Ramm, 1990, p. 223):

> Pray don't refer openly about yourself to Bertie [whose discretion she doubted]; the fewer [who] know anything the better and safer. Better send your letters for Sir Francis L[aking] [the Prince of Wales's physician] under cover to me or Beatrice and you had better write about your precious health on a *separate* sheet.

Of all her burdens, worry over the declining health of her firstborn, the child who had been closest to both herself and Albert, was among the heaviest to bear.

Because Queen Victoria's losses in the last years of her life were numerous and each in its way was of high emotional valence, these events must be regarded as important contributors to the etiology and perpetuation of the severe depression she experienced in the last five months of her life. The Queen confronted a succession of chronologically overlapping losses during the last five months of her life; one would be hard pressed to identify a two-month period within the five-month span covered by the final Journal volume during which a new or anticipated loss did not occur. At least in this one domain, Queen Victoria would hardly be considered unique; the cumulative emotional burden imposed by multiple losses is one she shared with many older individuals.

Nevertheless, no completely satisfactory conceptual models have been put forward to explain the contribution of personal loss to late-life depression. If there is a causal relationship, it is not universal; the experience of loss in old age may be commonplace, but, obviously, not everyone who has withstood such losses develops a major depression in late life. So having multiple bereavements in old age is probably best viewed as one risk factor among many for late-life depression, with the relative impact of the losses varying with each individual.

For Queen Victoria's late-life depression, a "threshold" model might be more fitting. Here the death of her adored grandson Christle in the fall of 1900, after so many important prior deaths, impresses the reader of her Journal as the loss from which she simply could not recover. However, a "vulnerability" model could also be in play in Her Majesty's reaction to this grandson's death, in the following way: For the Queen, Prince Christle's death occurred at the worst possible moment, precisely at a time when her anorexia, insomnia, blindness, debility, and likely cerebrovascular disease, were all becoming well established and consequential. For Queen Victoria, the principle of multiple vulnerabilities seemed to operate with special malevolence.

References

Lutyens, M. (Ed.). (1962). *Lady Lytton's court diary: 1895–1899.* Rupert Hart-Davis: London, UK, p. 90.

Ponsonby, F. (1898). *Letters from Sir F. Ponsonby to his mother (Westminster Papers), 26 Aug. 1898; 2 Sept. 1898.*

Pope-Hennessy, J. (1959). *Queen Mary.* George Allen & Unwin Limited: London, UK, p. 286.

Ramm, A. (Ed.). 1990. *Beloved & darling child: Last letters between Queen Victoria & her eldest daughter, 1896–1901.* Sutton Publishing, Stroud, UK, pp. 114, 221, 223.

Rose, K. (1984). *King George V.* Alfred A. Knopf, New York, NY, p. 48.

Weintraub, S. (1988). *Victoria: An intimate biography.* Truman Talley Books/ E.P. Dutton: New York, NY, pp. 363, 392.

10. Late-Life Depression and the Death of the Queen

From a contemporary standpoint, there is support, even if speculative, that cerebrovascular disease was both the underlying and the proximate cause of the Queen's death, with hemorrhagic stroke possibly providing the final blow. If so, depression was a critical co-factor.

The bi-phasic model proposed earlier still applies to Queen Victoria's last illness: The undetectable early stages of cerebrovascular disease, initiated and then perpetuated by inflammatory processes, had confounded the vulnerability to depression originally established by her first affective episode following Albert's death. Throughout the decades of the Queen's recovery from bereavement, these cerebrovascular-inflammatory factors operated *sub rosa*, as if lying in wait for the last year of the Queen's life, when she was almost continuously re-traumatized, experiencing loss after loss. Then, the weakness, anorexia, and insomnia associated with Her Majesty's late-life, or vascular depression, contributed to, set the stage for, later cerebral events and eventual fatality.

What role, if any, did chronic pain play? The aspect of Queen Victoria's arthritic pain is integrated into the overall picture with depression in a reciprocal fashion: That is, depression can accentuate the perception and experience of pain; and pain can in turn be an exacerbating factor in depression (Sheng, Liu, Wang, Cui, & Zhang, 2017).

This view of depression as a critical co-factor in Queen Victoria's decline and death may seem tendentious in the face of flawed sources of evidence—the subjective nature of the Journal, the unknown posthumous redactions by Princess Beatrice to this central document, and the lack of solid medical corroboration for the absence of malignancy, inflammatory disease, thyroid disorder, or any other alternative medical explanation for her rapid decline. Under these circumstances, depression is partly a diagnosis of exclusion. In addition, Sir James Reid's descriptions (those found in the materials not consigned to flames), upon which so many historians have depended, were ostensibly written for private consumption but may, like his official statements, have been influenced by personal ambition and political considerations.

All other factors aside, the reader of Queen Victoria's Journal cannot fail to be moved by Her Majesty's mournful mood as it unfolds in the final volume. Queen Victoria's old-age depression seemed to merit yet another book on her life among the hundreds already extant, as a psychiatric perspective on her last months has not been seriously considered in most accounts. That is not to say that the Queen's depression that emerged in the late summer of 1900 has gone completely unrecognized, but there has been little understanding by historians of the potentially lethal consequences of late-life depression; and the otherwise extensive scholarly research on the life and death of Queen Victoria largely omits consideration of this aspect.

Thus, the depiction of Queen Victoria's final illness and death presented in this book differs fundamentally from the impression held by many. Pope-Hennessy, in *Queen Mary*, describes the death of Queen Victoria as the "quiet fading out of life" (Pope-Hennessy, 1959, p. 353). It was surely not. On the contrary, Queen Victoria's last illness, however else it is characterized, was rapid and acute. From a basically healthy elderly woman with an active mind and a too-hearty appetite, over a five-month period, prodrome excluded, she lost at least half of her body weight to become the "tiny wasted figure in white" described by Pope-Hennessy himself (Pope-Hennessy, 1959, p. 353). The discredited notion of death as a "quiet fading out of life"—then and now only a wishful rumor about how old people actually die—is consistent with the view expressed by Marie Mallet that she, in turn, attributes to James Reid: "Sir J. Reid says if people live to 80 they may then go on for years and will only die of old age" (Mallet, 1968, p. 171).

Revisiting the importance of the Journal

What is most impressive to the reader of the Queen's Journal is the appalling extent of the hardships she endured. Depression stalked the Queen relentlessly from the fall of 1900 until her death. It is well accepted, almost too obvious to state, that exalted persons are not exempt from loss and depression, and yet, the extreme misery of the Queen-Empress and her remarkable ability to articulate it within the pages of her Journal create a memorable impression. In this regard, the emotionally unfiltered voice of Queen Victoria does not appear to have been substantially altered by Princess Beatrice's well-intentioned editing of the Journal; it seems improbable that the demure, unassuming Beatrice would have written in such an assertive tone. Queen Victoria was, if nothing else, emphatic about what she wanted and did not want, and her will went mostly unchallenged because no one (with the possible exception of the long-deceased Albert) dared contradict her.

In her Journal, as in her life, the Queen enjoyed a unique freedom from the limits on expression faced by ordinary individuals. It is difficult to weigh the impact made by the absence of such constraints. People, servants and the high-born alike, hung on every word uttered by the Sovereign. Rules made for others, even for her children as Princes and Princesses of the United Kingdom, did not apply to her.

Although one might say she was generally kind, the convenience, even the well-being, of others was never her foremost concern. In the particularly egregious example described previously in several different contexts, the Queen had felt that marital happiness of the kind she experienced with Albert should, if permitted at all for her youngest daughter Princess Beatrice, be subordinated to her sacrificial duty as helpmate to the monarch in old age. (The Queen later relented sufficiently to allow Beatrice to marry; but the widowed Princess eventually returned to assist her mother in her final years, and the Queen never seemed to notice or comment on her daughter's distress in this role). However, Queen Victoria's special freedom, together with a lifelong distaste for dissembling, are among the unique factors that lift Her Majesty's Journal writing from a mundane account of daily activities to, by the end, a moving testament of depressive suffering in old age.

Although Queen Victoria believed that she had the capacity to empathize with fellow mourners, her melancholia, as depicted in the Journal, had a distinctly narcissistic cast. After Albert's death in 1861, and for years after her recovery from his death, she presented herself as the *most* suffering of widows, the *most* miserable of God's creatures, someone who could understand, *more than anyone*, the special torment of losing by death those closest to them. Queen Victoria's tendency in the Journal is to present herself as the Romantic ideal of a sensitive, tormented soul, quite unlike the unfeeling, self-absorbed autocrat that she could also be at times. Some, but only some, of the narcissistic aspect may be explained by the unique position in which she found herself. As Sovereign, she was compelled to regard herself alternately as a person ("*I*") and as the embodiment of the State ("*We*"), even though her political influence was relatively narrow. It was from the point of view of "*I*" that most Journal entries were written, and the "*I*" was also the persona that very much feared death.

The Queen's depressive suffering

Some of the Queen's suffering, particularly the part attributable to functional decline, inanition, weakness and muscular atrophy, was the inevitable result of her own actions or inactions. Despite a tendency to hypochondriasis, in important ways she neglected her health. For much of her widowhood she overate (before her precipitous weight loss in the fall of 1900); and for the last five years of her life, or more, she was physically inactive to an extreme degree.

In addition, her mood and outlook were adversely influenced by her ruminative style of mourning. Queen Victoria always extended and prolonged mourning, insisting that every important death in her family be memorialized by statues of the departed one. The room in which Prince Albert had died in 1861 was left famously untouched for 40 years, his toothbrush and shaving materials all laid out in readiness, a fire re-lit in the grate every day. The Queen further mandated the strict observation of anniversaries, to the extent of recognizing the milestones of the deceased's friends and servants. Even for the time and place, such behavior was considered eccentric; but Queen Victoria's life had become organized around death. Her willful, histrionic nature and narcissistic focus, together with the inability of others to object, firmly established the joyless regime that prevailed in her Household for many years after Albert's death in 1861, easing only gradually with her recovery and with the birth of Princess Beatrice's children in the early 1890s. Ironically, Queen Victoria's attitude about death, with its oppressive piety, served to inhibit the more spontaneous and natural expressions of sadness that might have fostered an earlier recovery from mourning. The rites of bereavement may have been exaggerated, but genuine grieving was suppressed and, in consequence, prolonged.

Subjunctive history and the state of medical treatment in 1900

To a degree, Sir James Reid understood that Queen Victoria was depressed, but he did not fully appreciate the contribution of depression to her decline. (He and the seven-years-younger Sigmund Freud might possibly have crossed paths at the University of Vienna, at a time when Freud would have been an undergraduate and Reid had been pursuing post-graduate studies, but they came from entirely different worlds, and such a meeting seems unlikely).

It is tempting, however, to speculate that the Queen's rigid and unusually prolonged mourning might have masked hostile-ambivalent feelings toward her husband; the marital couple had experienced substantial intervals of disharmony during Albert's lifetime, although they tended to be retrospectively minimized by the Queen in her widowhood. For the Prince Consort, who had exchanged unfavorable prospects as a redundant younger son in Coburg for a position on the international stage, it had never been easy to accept a role in which he was technically a subject of his wife. But if Queen Victoria herself had experienced complex unresolved emotions regarding Albert, these could never have seen the light of day, both because the Queen had probably been unaware of them, and because the psychotherapeutic process of revealing unconscious motivations was in its infancy. In any event, even if it had been available, psychoanalysis would hardly have been a treatment she would have undertaken or tolerated. It should be remembered that even a routine physical examination would have been, for Queen Victoria, an unthinkable *lèse majesté*.

Even if he had made the conceptual connections for which he had not been trained, all Sir James had to offer the Queen by way of palliation were his own reassuring presence—not to suggest that this relationship and the positive psychological transference it entailed were unimportant, only that more was needed—and "draughts" of chlorodyne, Trional and other sedatives, including hot tea laced with whiskey. The effects of these medications and interventions should not be entirely discounted, especially the potency of the doctor–patient relationship, but neither did they represent specific, targeted treatment for depression.

Then, another hypothetical question arises: Would this previously vigorous woman have survived longer, functioned better, or otherwise experienced symptomatic relief, from 21st-century therapeutic and preventative interventions? Not only from serotonin-enhancing antidepressants but from what is now a conventional regimen of medications controlling blood pressure, lipids and triglyceride levels, anticoagulants when atrial fibrillation is present, and, if necessary, the addition of exogenous thyroid hormone or dopamine? A simple exercise program and attention to diet? A reduction of diabetic risk? The answers are surely unknowable.

To indulge further in what has been called "subjunctive history" (James, 1997), one can ask whether Queen Victoria might have lived a decade longer had she not contracted a depression so severe. What then might have been the consequences? Queen Victoria, it need hardly be told, was a figure of paramount importance. Although her actual powers were few and limited, she was the embodiment of the state, the dean of government, and the face of the nation and Empire. Her personal influence on the broader international stage was arguably even greater, as her 36 grandchildren made important marriages across the European continent. Two of these grandchildren had, in Queen Victoria's lifetime, assumed world-changing roles, namely, the German Kaiser Wilhelm and the Empress Alexandra of Russia, although in both instances with disastrous endgames. However, if Queen Victoria had survived longer into the first decade of the twentieth century, a realistic enough prospect even with 19th-century health practices and an element of luck, then it is possible to speculate that the Kaiser, who feared his formidable grandmother, might have softened the inflammatory rhetoric and behavior that eventually broke the peace of Europe. As it was, Sir James Reid's adept management of the despised Kaiser's presence at Queen Victoria's deathbed may have averted an earlier international crisis.

"It is a great & glorious thought…."

As head of state, Queen Victoria was shrewd, but mainly she was consistent, adhering initially to principles laid down by Prince Albert before his death, principles which he himself was likely to have amended had he not died prematurely. Writing to her uncle King Leopold of Belgium on Christmas Eve 1861, ten days after Albert's death, she had declared that "…*his* wishes—*his* plans—about everything, *his* views about *every* thing are to be my law! And *no human power* will make me swerve from *what he* decided and wished…." (Weintraub, 1988, p. 307).

Inevitably her absence from public view for so many years after Prince Albert's death contributed to the erosion of the Sovereign's remaining prerogatives and at the same time helped to consolidate the mostly symbolic style of constitutional monarchy seen in the United Kingdom today. Even so, by the end of Queen Victoria's reign, there were no doubts about her superior command of her role or her adroitness, either with or apart from Albert. If there were any concerns lingering on from the reigns of her predecessors Queens Mary II and Anne about the ability of a woman to be an effective Queen Regnant, Queen Victoria put them firmly to rest.

Queen Victoria the person had a propensity for truth and a gift for friendship, both characteristics that drew people to her and, in some cases, bound them for life. The Queen well knew how deep were her gifts, aside from her position. What she did not fully grasp, perhaps as a result of native narcissism accentuated by the extraordinary circumstances of her life, were her own limitations and contradictions. She retained an air of rectitude, inflexibility, and absolutism which even major depression in late life did not at first moderate. Her deviations from constitutional neutrality were few but tended to be flagrant. This rigid conviction of the rightness of her views was sometimes the cause of misjudgment but could also be taken as her chief asset; and it had seen her through many trials, first emerging when, as an adolescent princess, she called up a bold resistance to the bullying of her mother's malicious comptroller Sir John Conroy.

Even if she had been blind to her shortcomings, in many ways Queen Victoria's firmness was her greatness, the source of the moral courage that defined both her private character and her public image. But by the end of her life, depression, weakness and cognitive loss had completed the destruction of her distinctive personality. So in her final weeks, helpless and terrified, at the end delirious, this woman who had been raised without a father* leaned heavily on an idealized relationship with male authority, personified by Sir James Reid, and on the essentially illusory intimacy of the doctor–patient relationship.

But beyond the Monarch and the person, Queen Victoria lives on as an historical legend; in that role she is the perpetual and far less complicated Widow of Windsor. In a letter of consolation to a more recent British Queen who was also for many years a widow, HM Queen Elizabeth the Queen Mother, the Rev. Anthony Harbottle (Harbottle, 2000) captured the essence of Queen Victoria's post-Albert credo, beliefs to which she adhered throughout her years of bereavement, recovery and late-life depression:

> There is no separation but an abiding oneness with our loved ones who have gone on ahead & are ever with us…. It is a great & glorious thought, as Your Majesty knows so well.

---

* Queen Victoria's father, Prince Edward, Duke of Kent (4th son of King George III), died of pneumonia when she was 8 months old. Her mother did not remarry.

References

Harbottle, A. (2000). *Letter from Rev. Anthony Harbottle to Queen Elizabeth The Queen Mother (Harbottle Papers), 3 February 2000.*

James, L. (1997). *Raj: The making and unmaking of British India.* St. Martin's Griffin: New York, NY, p. 647.

Mallet, V. (Ed.). (1968). *Life with Queen Victoria: Marie Mallet's letters from court, 1887–1901.* Houghton Mifflin Company: Boston, MA, p. 171.

Pope-Hennessy, J. (1959). *Queen Mary.* George Allen & Unwin Limited: London, UK, p. 353.

Sheng, J., Liu, S., Wang, Y., Cui, R., & Zhang, X. (2017). The link between depression and chronic pain. *Neural Plasticity.* Pub. Online June 19, 2017. https://doi: 10.1155/2017/9724371

Weintraub, S. (1988). *Victoria: An intimate biography.* Truman Talley Books/ E.P. Dutton: New York, NY, p. 307.

Appendix 1: Locations

In August, 1900, the eighty-one-year-old Queen Victoria was still in residence at Osborne House on the Isle of Wight, shortly to depart for what was to be her last late-summer-to-autumn sojourn at Balmoral Castle in Scotland. Keeping to her customary fixed calendar of migrations to her principal homes, she remained at Balmoral until 7 November, when she left for Windsor. After observing the 39th anniversary of the Prince Consort's death on 14 December with a service at the family mausoleum at Frogmore on the grounds of Windsor Castle, on the 18th she returned to Osborne, where she usually celebrated Christmas. There she was to die on 22 January 1901.

Appendix 2: Key Royal Family Names*

In her Journal Queen Victoria often referred to her nine children and 36 grandchildren by various nicknames, many of which were originated by the Queen and used intimately *en famille.*

The Queen's children, in order of birth, were:

Princess Victoria, Princess Royal, by marriage the Empress Frederick of Germany, known as **"Vicky."**

Prince Albert Edward, Prince of Wales, later King Edward VII, known as **"Bertie."**

---

* More detailed biographical details of Royal family members, courtiers, political office-holders, and friends, are footnoted throughout the text.

Princess Alice, by marriage the Grand Duchess of Hesse and by Rhine.

Prince Alfred, Duke of Edinburgh and also Duke of Coburg, known as **"Affie."**

Princess Helena, by marriage Princess Christian of Schleswig-Holstein-Sonderberg-Augustenberg, known as **"Lenchen."**

Princess Louise, by marriage the Marchioness of Lorne and later the Duchess of Argyll.

Prince Arthur, the Duke of Connaught and Strathearn.

Prince Leopold, the Duke of Albany.

Princess Beatrice, by marriage Princess Henry of Battenberg.

By August 1900, Princess Alice and the Princes Leopold and Alfred had died; the Empress Frederick was dying of cancer in Germany.

Other family members mentioned in Queen Victoria's personal Journal are recorded below. Each family member is listed under the name of the child to whom he or she is related.

Victoria ("Vicky")

Princess Victoria (Princess Royal) married Crown Prince Frederick, later the Emperor Frederick III, known as "Fritz." The Fredericks' infamous son was Kaiser Wilhem II, known to his English relatives as "William" or "Willie." One of their daughters, Princess Margaret of Prussia, was known as "Mossy."

Albert Edward, Prince of Wales, later King Edward VII ("Bertie")

Prince Albert Edward (Prince of Wales), known in the family as "Bertie," married Princess Alexandra of Denmark ("Alix") who became Princess of Wales and later Queen Alexandra. The Wales' second son, Prince George of Wales, Duke of York, known as "Georgie," later became Prince of Wales after his father and eventually succeeded as King George V. Prince George's wife, born Princess Victoria Mary ("May") of Teck, was by marriage successively the Duchess of York, Duchess of Cornwall and York, Princess of Wales and Queen Mary.

Alice

Princess Alice married Louis, the Grand Duke of Hesse and by Rhine. The Louis' son Ernest, known as "Ernie," succeeded his father as Grand Duke. Among the daughters of Princess Alice and her husband were Princess Alix of Hesse, known as "Alicky," who by marriage to Tsar Nicholas II ("Nicky"), became the Tsarina Alexandra of Russia. Several other daughters of Princess Alice and Grand Duke Louis were Princess Victoria of Hesse, by marriage Princess Louis of Battenberg, sometimes referred to as "Victoria Battenberg," or "Victoria B"; and Princess Irene of Hesse, by marriage Princess Henry of Prussia.

Alfred ("Affie")

Prince Alfred, Duke of Edinburgh and Duke of Coburg, known as "Affie," married the Grand Duchess Marie of Russia, sometimes referred to as "Marie Edinburgh." The Edinburghs' son was another Prince Alfred, known as "young Alfred." Affie's daughter Princess Victoria Melita of Edinburgh and Coburg, known as "Ducky," married (first) Princess Alice's son Ernest, the Grand Duke of Hesse and by Rhine. Another Edinburgh-Coburg daughter, Princess Marie, became Queen Marie of Romania through her marriage to King Ferdinand.

Helena ("Lenchen")

Princess Helena married Prince Christian of Schleswig-Holstein-Sonderberg-Augustenberg. The Christians' daughters included the Princesses Helena Victoria and Marie Louise of Schleswig-Holstein, the former known as "Thora," and the latter as "Louie." Princess Helena's older son was Prince Christian Victor of Schleswig-Holstein, known as "Christle." (The lengthy territorial modifier "Schleswig-Holstein-Sonderberg-Augustenberg" is frequently simplified to "Schleswig-Holstein.")

Louise

Princess Louise married the Marquess of Lorne, known as "Lorne," later Duke of Argyll. They had no children.

Arthur

Prince Arthur (Duke of Connaught) married Princess Louise of Prussia, known by the German diminutive "Louischen." Princess Louise, by marriage the Duchess of Connaught, is to be distinguished from two other royal Louises: Queen Victoria's daughter the Marchioness of Lorne and her granddaughter Princess Louise of Wales.

Leopold

Prince Leopold (Duke of Albany) married Princess Helen of Waldeck-Pyrmont. The Albanys' children were Princess Alice of Albany and Prince Charles Edward of Albany, the former known as "Alice," and the latter known as "Little Charlie" or "Charlie Albany." Prince Charles Edward of Albany became the Duke of Albany after his father's death and also Duke of Saxe-Coburg and Gotha after the death of his uncle Prince Alfred.

Beatrice

Princess Beatrice married Prince Henry of Battenberg, known as "Liko." Among the Henry Battenbergs' four children were Prince Alexander of Battenberg, known as "Drino"; and Princess Victoria Eugenia of Battenberg, later the Queen of Spain, known as "Ena," the last of her given names. Princess Beatrice's husband Liko Battenberg was a brother of Prince Louis of Battenberg, husband of Princess Alice's daughter, Princess Victoria of Hesse.

Photo Credits

1. ACFB78 Prince Alfred, Duke of Edinburgh and Saxe Coburg Gotha, 1844 – 1900.
2. BEDM99 QUEEN VICTORIA and her daughter Princess Beatrice in 1880.
3. C548GR Princess Victoria Mary, aka Princess May, later Queen consort of the United Kingdom as the wife of King George V. Mary of Teck.
4. GR11JY Prince Christian Victor of Schleswig-Holstein, 1867 – 1900. Eldest son of Princess Helena, third daughter of Queen Victoria.
5. KRCYYG PRINCESS HELENA VICTORIA Princess Helen Victoria of Schleswig-Holstein, daughter of Princess Helena & Prince Christian, grandaughter of Queen Victoria. Date: 1870 – 1948.
6. MR38JR Portrait of Sir James Reid, 1st Baronet (1849–1923) a French physician to three British monarchs. Dated 19th century.
7. W7d60a Prince Henry of Battenberg, (1900).Artist: Theodor Prumm.
8. Hft0fy EDWARD VII (1841–1910) as Prince of Wales about 1890.
9. Ddm847 Princess Alexandra of Denmark (later Queen Consort to King Edward VII), 1862. Artist: Unknown.

Index

illness, 115, 117
James Reid and, 115–17, 119–20,
132, 133, 139, 141, 148,
172–74
Victoria and, 115–17, 119–20, 133,
172–74
Ridley, Matthew White (1st Viscount
Ridley), 48, 63
Roberts, Frederick (1st Earl Roberts),
26, 33, 39, 40, 48, 71, 112–13
positions held by, 17n, 39–40, 76,
112–13
Prince Arthur and, 39–40, 122
Prince Christle and, 17, 113
reception in London, 118–19
South African War and, 112–13,
119
Victoria and, 21–22, 26, 33, 39,
40, 71, 112–13, 118–19, 122,
128–29
Roxburghe, "Annie" (Anne Innes-Ker,
Duchess of Roxburghe), 43
Royal Mausoleum, Frogmore, 83, 84,
94n
Victoria's trips to, 68–70, 82–84, 94
Russell, Emily. See Ampthill, Emily

Salisbury, Lord (Robert Gascoyne-
Cecil, 3rd Marquess of Salisbury),
16, 16n, 46–47
cabinet, 8, 25n, 43, 46–48, 58, 60
Marie Mallet on, 46–47
positions held by, 16, 25n, 43, 46,
58n
Victoria and, 8, 16, 43, 46–48, 58,
60, 73, 84, 94, 167
servants, 171–73
Prince Affie's attitudes toward, 22,
100–101
Victoria's relations with, 33, 100–
101, 103, 115, 171–73
See also specific servants

sleep, Queen Victoria's, 31, 73, 76, 77,
84, 99, 101, 105, 108–12, 114, 131
efforts to induce, 60, 78, 98–99,
104, 105, 114, 146 (see also
draughts)
insomnia, restlessness, and
disrupted sleep, 2, 10, 52, 60,
61, 72–73, 78–79, 84, 98–99,
104–6, 108–11, 111n, 114,
123, 130
pain and, 60, 72–73
South African War. See Boer War/
South African War
Stephen, Sir Condie, 23–25
Strachey, Lytton, 5, 144

Teck, Alge. See Alexander Cambridge
Teck, Frank. See Francis of Teck
Teck princess. See Mary (May) of Teck
Thora, Princess. See Helena Victoria of
Schleswig-Holstein
"threshold" model, 187
Turi (Italian Spitz), 139

vascular depression
defined, 158
See also under depression of Queen
Victoria
Victoria, Queen, 142–43
accidents, 181
animals and, 70, 71, 139
attire and fashion, 176
dresses, 1, 161, 169, 170
jewelry, 169–70
attraction to male servants, 100,
171
childhood, 197
climbing Craig Gowan, 181
dancing, 169, 182
death, 135–37, 142–44
"a dying woman," 97, 104

Robert C. Abrams, M.D., is a graduate of the University of California, Berkeley, and Mount Sinai (now Icahn) School of Medicine in New York City. He currently practices psychiatry at Weill Cornell Medicine in New York, where he has received numerous awards for clinical teaching as Professor of Psychiatry in Medicine. Dr Abrams's research interests have been focused on old-age psychiatry, including personality disorders, depression, suicidality, and the humanities. Since 2016 Dr. Abrams has also been a film reviewer for the British Medical Journal/Medical Humanities. The present monograph stems from his lifelong interest in 19th and 20th-century English history and from a series of published papers on the last years of Queen Victoria's reign.

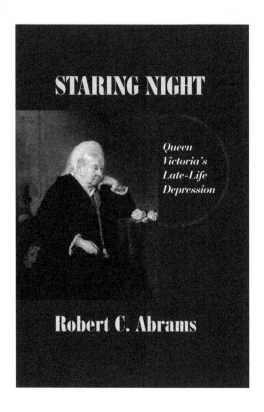

It is perhaps the famous portrait by the Austrian painter Heinrich von Angeli that best encompasses Queen Victoria's dual post-Albert identities as widow and Queen Regnant, displaying her black mourner's dress and lace bridal veil, as well as the Sovereign's distinctive Garter sash. This portrait was commissioned in 1899, at a time when Queen Victoria was free from serious depression, having largely recovered from her prolonged grief over Prince Albert's death by the early 1880s. Nevertheless, the Queen's facial expression in the von Angeli portrait evokes weariness and vulnerability. Reproduced on the cover of this book, the picture also portends Victoria's immediate future: In the final five months of her life the Queen was to be in a continuous state of mourning as new losses mounted.

CPSIA information can be obtained
at www.ICGtesting.com
Printed in the USA
BVHW091055151120
593221BV00004B/80

9 781949 093551